D1596393

FIRST PULSE

By Dr. Merrill Garnett

Paintings by Joy Garnett
Edited by Bill Jones

First Pulse Projects, Inc.
New York

First Pulse Projects, Inc.
P.O. Box 1269
Canal Street Station
New York, NY 10013
http://www.firstpulseprojects.org
info@firstpulseprojects.org

Library of Congress Catalogue Number: 2001097428

2nd Edition, November 2001
ISBN 0-9665597-1-1

Book Design by Bill Jones.

Printed in the United States of America

To the loving memory of my sister
Carol Abraham.

Contents

Paintings in oil on canvas by Joy Garnett

Foreword

My association with Merrill Garnett over the last several years has been a remarkable experience. Merrill is a person of unique energy, focus and persistence. He is a true original—a person in pursuit of a profoundly humane goal along career and personal paths quite unlike anyone else I have ever met. Merrill is one of the rare individuals for whom "doing well by doing good" isn't a superficial slogan but rather is truly second nature.

In this book Merrill has produced a fascinating, intensely personal account of his forty year quest for effective cancer treatments. I'm sure most readers will react to the book as I did. I was engaged and captivated—both at the personal and at the scientific levels. In this era of bureaucratized science, people with uniquely individual creative vision like Merrill are increasingly rare and increasingly important. Readers are treated to a deep, clear look into this world.

In the course of his quest Merrill has generated and tested an enormous, diverse array of organo-metallic compounds—culminating in a palladium/lipoic acid complex that apparently has remarkable properties. Merrill recruited members of my group and myself several years ago to contribute to understanding in detail how his palladium/lipoic acid complex worked at the cellular level. Early in these studies we were astonished to discover not only how specific a cytotoxic agent the complex was but also that the details of its behavior indicated that it might be the first example of a long sought new class of highly specific anticancer agents.

To understand how exciting the properties of the palladium/lipoic acid complex are it is necessary to appreciate the context. As Merrill discusses at length in the chapters that follow, it has been known since the work of Warburg early in this century that the energy metabolism of most cancer cells is remarkably different than that of normal cells. This difference and some other properties of cancers strongly suggest that cancer cells undergo an illicit, permanent activation of a cellular regulatory program that is normally activated only briefly and reversibly in healthy cells during the process of wound healing. The energy metabolism of cancer cells looks like it has undergone a permanent regulatory adaptation to growth under conditions of low oxygen such as normally prevail in and immediately surrounding a fresh wound in healthy tissue but also exist in tumors.

Though our knowledge here is still quite incomplete we have some useful information about what this change entails. In particular, an enzyme complex—pyruvate dehydrogenase (PDH)—occupying a pivotal point in deciding whether energy is extracted from glucose anaerobically (without use of oxygen) or aerobically (using oxygen) is apparently altered in cancer cells. Thus, targeting the altered form of PDH in cancer cells might represent a highly specific way to inhibit or kill these cells. To clinicians and basic scientists this is a most appealing prospect. However, no one had previously found a way to bring this approach to fruition.

PDH is one of only a very few cellular enzyme complexes to make use of the coenzyme lipoic acid. This suggests that it might be practical to develop lipoic acid derivatives that would allow the specific targeting of cancer cells through their altered PDH. Strikingly, lipoic acid is an essential component of Merrill's palladium/lipoic acid complex. Moreover, our studies in cultured cells strongly suggest that the complex may specifically inhibit tumor cell PDH. The palladium/lipoic acid complex thus behaves as if it might be the hoped for "bullet" for cancer cell energy metabolism.

At the end of the book is a short Appendix summarizing the work we carried out with the support of Garnett McKeen Laboratory and the Carol M. Baldwin Breast Cancer Research Fund. This report is primarily intended to give professional biologists and physicians an understanding of where these studies stand and why we are excited by their prospects.

Traditionally trained biologists will generally not accept all of Merrill's theoretical views of how cells use electrical energy or of how this can be manipulated with therapeutic agents. He approaches these matters with the intuition of a highly trained inorganic electrochemist. However, it is important to understand that this is a relatively unimportant issue in the present context. What matters is the practical outcome.

In conclusion, we strongly suspect that Merrill Garnett has developed the first agent capable of exploiting the extremely attractive therapeutic target presented by the altered energy metabolism of malignant cells. If so, it will be a momentous achievement in the long history of research in cancer therapy. We are pleased to have made a small contribution to his quest.

Paul M. Bingham
Department of Biochemistry and Cell Biology
State University of New York
Stony Brook, New York
May, 1998

Editor's Preface

We all know what cancer does. I watched my father die from it when I was a boy. Oncologists know every intricacy of its devastating path through the body and have hundreds of names for its effects. Medical science has been trying to stop or limit those effects for many years. Recently there has been much talk and press about possible cures, but with all the study and all the effort little is known about the origins of the disease.

It was during a drive to Fire Island that I first heard Dr. Garnett speak of cancer cells as anaerobic clones and then go on to say he saw cancer as embryo cells that can't make the next transition toward mature differentiated tissue. The view of glistening water stretching far into the distance seemed to reverberate with Dr. Garnett's expansive vision. After a lifetime of fearing the unknown—the mysterious killer that wiped out much of my family—I finally heard someone begin to explain what the disease was.

Speculation aside, what must be understood about Dr. Garnett is that he is first and foremost a scientist. Though his medical discoveries point toward a different path, in terms of the gene mechanism and a restorative therapy in cancer, they are, by all accounts, a part of mainstream science. Dr. Garnett has synthesized a molecule (the palladium/lipoic acid complex, on which he holds three patents), a stable chemical product, using, at times, what might be termed "industrial methods." In his desire to search everywhere for a safe, non-toxic chemotherapy, Dr. Garnett followed the path to industrial chemistry and corrosion engineering. Who would have thought that an industry that has brought us so many carcinogenic materials could hold answers to saving lives.

On a warm spring day in 1959, while sitting in his newly finished suburban kitchen, Dr. Garnett, just discharged after 4 years as a naval dentist, knew that he would devote his life to cancer research. He would not take the worn paths, but would find a non-toxic way to stem the disease. He had had a number of personal experiences that made him believe it was possible to understand the disease in a visceral way. He came to believe that the path to this understanding lay in restoring something that was missing, rather than attacking the genetic material which, even during this early period of chemotherapy research, had become the standard course.

Fundamentally, Dr. Garnett's inquiry is concerned with the energy flow into the DNA. He sees this energy flow not as some deep mystery of the cosmos, but in simple terms, electrically, like the systems that power our lights and TVs. This idea was rooted in certain views present in the scientific literature at the time. Based on this perspective, he began to make metallo-organic compounds, screening them on the Ehrlich carcinoma in mice for both toxicity and effectiveness as anti-tumor agents.

Imagine if you will 30 years of "cooking" compounds, and injecting mice only to find that the materials are toxic, ineffective as anti-tumor agents, or unstable as chemical compounds. Imagine 13 years of making vanadium compounds which, he says, "led me on only to dump me in the end" like a fickle lover. Imagine then, late one night, Dr. Garnett going down to his basement lab as he has so many nights before. By using the electrochemical tests he has learned from corrosion engineering, he is able to demonstrate the electrical efficiency of the molecular shunts he has been constructing. That night, he gets the most important reading of his life: the palladium/lipoic acid compound—one he has just begun to work with—transfers energy to DNA more efficiently than anything he's seen in 30 years of electrochemical analysis.

Holding back his excitement lest he be "dumped" once again, he injects 12 mice with the Ehrlich carcinoma as he has done thousands of times before. A few days later, as the mouse bellies are beginning to swell with tumor, he injects six of them with the palladium complex and retires for the night. The next morning he runs downstairs expecting to find what he has found so many times before—that the mice are dead and gone, buried deep in the sawdust at the bottom of their cage. But no, the mice are running around. Within a week, the treated mice are rid of the swellings, while the controls—the six untreated mice—are dead.

In 1990, some 30 years and 20,000 metallo-organic compounds later, after a journey of persistence that led him through years of research down unknown paths, Dr. Garnett synthesized the first non-toxic, anti-tumor agent: palladium/lipoic acid. At the time of this writing, after eight years of animal testing and refinement to assure that the compound is not toxic, even at fifty times the normal dose, he is taking the material into FDA testing on human patients.

This book works to reveal linkages between art and science. Dr. Garnett's daughter, Joy, initially trained as a scientist and later as an artist. She paints images of things we can never actually see, but which are shown to exist by science. Her paintings are reproduced as a way to enter the text. They explore how visual representations influence scientific research by presenting that research to a public that must eventually support it.

This book is a collaborative work of art that endeavors to facilitate scientific understanding for the benefit of both art and science. I am delighted to have been able to help in its realization.

Bill Jones
June, 1998

Introduction to the Second Edition

This book was written as a personal journey. But it was the personal journey of many souls. It came to be woven by individuals caught up with me in the mission and the science, and the questions about our own limits in making changes in the world.

It also became obvious that large emotional and historic forces were involved. I receive calls from all over the world from physicians, scientists, and patients. These enrich our information background. They also challenge the consistency and the basis of my work. And they force our group to open our understanding and to add to it and refine it. We are reminded that the literature and laboratories of the medical science world are bought and paid for by the pain and grief of those trapped by disease.

There have been special people here who made things happen. My wife who I met in a Navy Hospital in 1955 has been my strongest supporter. She knew and accepted that the research came before other comforts. She watched her mother die of breast cancer in Egypt from an aggressive tumor that killed suddenly, even as they planned their trip to come to the U.S. for treatment. And so my wife worked with me in laboratories, learning to inject mice, and doing the more difficult cleaning among nasty odors. Our two children came to the labs and worked to help, and more importantly they supplied the enthusiasm and faith we needed to work and to discover. My partner Roy McKeen arrived by fate in the mid seventies. He provided boundless energy and organizational skill so that we could form a company out of thin air and no income and go forward. Then my friends and relatives chipped in and we bought some lab instruments.

The mice stopped dying in the early nineties. It was the palladium/lipoic acid polymer that did it. I spent a couple of years optimizing the structure and formulation. Then some Veterinarians studied it in cats with tumors. There were dramatic remissions that caused great excitement and produced long distance telephone calls that came out of nowhere. One of these brought me to Toronto and the Falk Clinic. Dr. Rudy Falk was Professor of Surgery at the University of Toronto. He had established a private Oncology Clinic that attracted patients from around the world. In addition to mainstream chemotherapy and surgery, he tested alternative medicines and investigative medicines in attempts to help patients who had run out of treatment options. He was thought of as a maverick for this reason, but his skills, experience, and publications were extensive. He had access to tumor screening labs at the University of Toronto, and after studying the compound for a few weeks he told me that it tested similarly to my own tests in mice. Yes, it was enormously safe. And yes, it could knock out tumors—in this case a vicious mast cell tumor. Rudy had a modern state-of the-art medication preparation room with trained technicians. We would synthesize the material there on weekends. It was not long before Rudy introduced the substance into clinical investigation in his clinic. This was followed by a host of remissions in gravely advanced cases. Thus, the clinical investigations, albeit limited, had begun.

This second edition of *First Pulse* coincides with the start of the next stage of the journey. The stage has two aspects. Primary in our responsibility is the achievement of the formal standards for pharmaceutical use in the United States. These standards, referred to by a variety of acronyms such as cGMP, and CMC, along with preliminary clinical data and protocols, encompass the submission request to the Food and Drug Administration to do a controlled clinical trial. The legal guidelines are described in a book called CFR 21. A scan reading of CFR 21 quickly impresses one not only with the enormous number of details and thoroughness of this process, but of the fundamental relevance of the compliance undertaking. The underlying principles are safety and effectiveness of new medicines.

The other aspect is the growth of our research to a new level of understanding. We refer to this stage as *electrogenetics*. No amount of pharmaceutical compliance can achieve a major advance without some underlying new level of basic scientific understanding. I have added a chapter on electrogenetics at the end of this book. One of the keys to this view is the discovery of an energetic process which edits the genome during the life of the organism. This process of Paramagnetic Editing will be reported in the Journal literature shortly. This reaction can account for maturation and development and aging. If it is real, then failure of such a reaction readily accounts for malignant transformations. If it is real, a variety of new medicines can be designed to maintain and restore the electrogenetic reactions of the body. This is our direction.

Dr. Merrill Garnett
September 2001

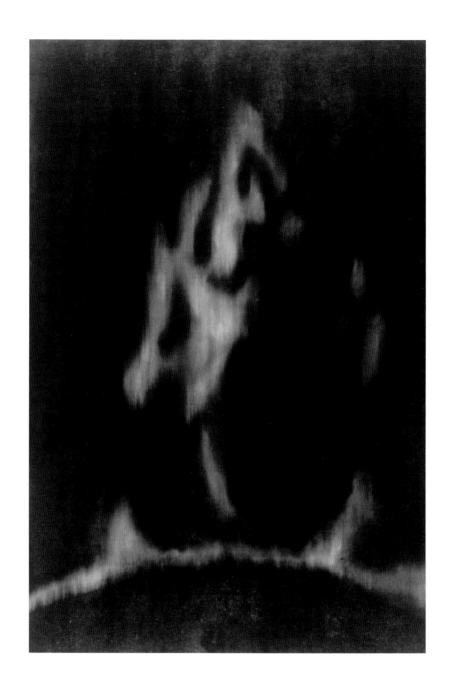

Introduction to the First Edition

In 1959, after discharging from the military as a naval dentist, I went back to graduate school to study molecular biology. At that time we were all in love with the DNA helix. It was the way and the light. We thought studying it would open the genetic secrets of disease and in particular cancer. So we leapt in and learned about transcription, translation, and transduction, and we learned about the abilities of certain compounds to interfere with these processes. We looked for the disease, but didn't find it.

As the years went by genetics enlarged, and the papers proliferated. The language grew to include symbolic representations of the disease like the oncogene, and the hope grew that there would now be a narrower focus that would yield understanding and healing. But the symbolic language didn't deliver what had been promised.

Years passed, and the suppressor enzymes came to the fore with the promise that there might be a gene sequence that can control cancer, but as of yet little has come from it. Hope is beginning to fade. We are left with the model of inheritance, which involves the storage of information and its retrieval related to certain large biological molecules. And we are wondering why, since we know so much about information storage and retrieval, we cannot get out the information that relates to cancer. We wonder why the thrust of pharmacology in medicine involves the same toxic elements in the medications used for that disease, so that in the treatment of cancer we still use blocking agents, inhibiting agents, and toxic agents. This tells us that in essential principles we have not defined the process separately from the rest of the organism, so that in order to stop the growth of cancer we are forced to stop the entire organism in its tracks and bring it to the point of death.

In science we use the term paradigm for a model of a way of thinking. If we look at our genetic model we will see that it parallels that of the computer. Our thinking on computers is very close to our thinking on genetics. We see them both as mechanisms for the storage and retrieval of information. Are they or are they not?

The hard drive and the DNA are the deep storage; the conservative elements to be transmitted. The RNA is the working model, the somewhat more dynamic expression of the selections from the deep storage to do the job. The keyboard is the environment eliciting, with its signals, responses from the stored information. We have worked with that model since the 1950s, and it does not bear out. I think the model is correct but incomplete. The question is: Why is it not complete enough to give us what we want in terms of medicine?

I went back and looked at my computer. The typical problems I have with it concern connectivity by special cables to its outputs—its printers, its scan-

ners, its external drives. Power is needed to drive the information, and the electronic carriers of that power can be defective and can characterize what we now see as genetic disease. We should consider that one of the things that both genes and computers do, in addition to storing and retrieving information, is store and retrieve energy in a highly discriminating way.

I see cancer as an embryo cell that can't make the next transition. This idea of disease as a failure to mature is an old one, and it has to be clarified in detail. There are three major events in maturation that I know of (and I'm sure there are many more that I haven't considered) that have to do with energy flow in the cell. There are a number of major enzymatic events that have to be expressed in order for energy to flow. That's just to get it started. And then for the maintenance of that flow there's an enormous number of, shall we say, stock enzymes that run to do the job. So when the impedance is wrong–impedance being the current at that resistance which is dependent on particular frequencies for its transmission–or the wire breaks, you have to change the impedance or restore the connection. This is what palladium DNA reductase, the molecule we developed in the 1990s, does.

The discovery of the palladium complex as a therapeutic metallo-organic agent suggests that there are many more mysterious catalytic metals that may well be utilized by living organisms for growth. There also may be alternative pathways that can be substituted for existing enzymes in case there are genetic defects. The periodic table is so extensive it invites a great deal of work with metals in the body. What we're now trying to do is to discover the electrical schematic at the cellular level. I never dreamed that the reactions were so organized and concerted. What we have in the palladium complex is a molecular electronic device.

Hematologists used to refer to a shift toward the primitive as a shift to the left. This is the classical language. I always wanted to reverse this shift. This is much more difficult than selective toxicity. It has to emerge as the science that made it possible emerges. And now we have a palladium-based electrical pathway that holds the promise of many pathways in restorative biochemistry. We're going to put back what is missing in a non-toxic way. We're going to complete the electrogenetic pulse that's found in all the higher living forms, in our cells, and in our physiology. If we can restore that pulse, we also restore the confidence that we are part of a continuum of energy flow in nature that is intimate to the emergence of organisms. Information storage and transfer, and energy storage and transfer, are behind the dynamic of nature and biology. If we come to understand this dynamic then we will have a much larger chapter in biochemistry than we had envisioned.

This brief narrative of discovery is as much about the somewhat personal and at times unorthodox ways of thinking that led me to questions concerning the first pulse, as it is an explanation of what I found. I am thankful for this opportunity to blur boundaries while looking for meanings.

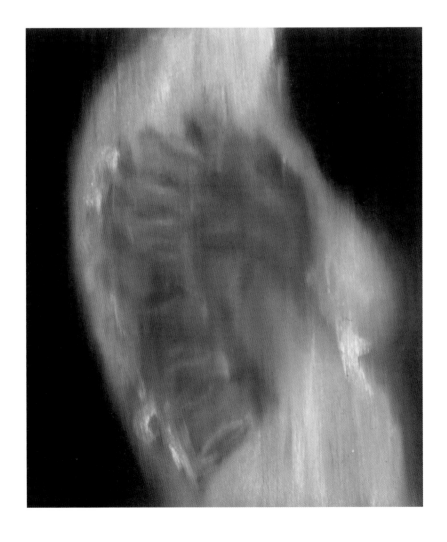

18

1. Proud Flesh

The auditorium seemed cavernous as the overhead lights dimmed to black. The hematologist pulled the projection screen down with a force intended to catch the attention of the Navy interns gathering for yet another class at St. Albans Hospital. Suddenly an arc lamp shot a beam of light across the darkness. There, projected on the screen, were the brilliantly stained cancer cells of the bone marrow. But the screen couldn't hold them and they overflowed onto the walls and poured out onto the floor. At that moment on a winter day in 1955, something happened that touched my inner being. I had recognized something in that visualization of the cancer cell which identified the disease as something that could be understood viscerally from the inside out. This visual event brought back memories of my father, a general practitioner, and X-rays with dim shadows I didn't understand. He would show me the dark sheets of X-ray film, and say sad things like, "She's so young," or "He doesn't deserve this." I guess I was the nearest soul and he needed someone to talk to. I held on to the dim memories, yet when I decided to redirect my life the decision surprised me. I remember sitting in the kitchen of my new house in Farmingdale, Long Island. My wife, Hoda, had just finished making curtains for the windows and the sun was streaming in. I felt a glow within me that matched the light outside. I knew at that moment that I would do cancer research. It seemed that the visual power, the identity of the disease, had been made clear to me as a symbolic event, an electrical event in my perception of who I was, though I still don't know why.

Going back to school wasn't in my plans. After being discharged from active duty in the Navy, I thought I would practice in the suburbs and play tennis and have a garden, a lawn, and crabgrass. Things were different then. Many of my father's patients were our friends. Some of them owed him money. He never worried about it. "I'm their health insurance," he'd say. There were four dentists and three physicians in my family. I used to visit them often in their offices. They were a pretty social bunch, and had very personal habits and ways of dealing with their patients. Their medical legacy was to be passed on to their children who would be physicians and dentists. It would be fun and music and air conditioning. That was what I had been brought up to be and it seemed natural. I never expected to go back to school to study chemistry or to have laboratory mice in my basement. But everything changed.

Graduate school was difficult, at first, because I already had a wife and the beginnings of a family to support, but I was going to do research. Somehow it would work out. I would work longer hours, and we would fit it in. Every course I took, whether it was botany or cell morphology, I would somehow write papers on cancer, such as "Development of Plant Tumors," "Genetic Transduction in Tumor Formation," or "The Interactions of Tumor Virus."

At the same time, I was fortunate to find a position as a dentist at Central Islip State Hospital on Long Island. I could pay for classes and support my family. It was the perfect situation. Central Islip had a research division, and they saw me as a person already involved in research. I got in on the ground floor. They didn't pay very much, so there wasn't a lot of competition for the job. But it gave me a great opportunity, because there were very few academic positions for dentists. I must have shown my enthusiasm to them before they employed me, because they gladly sent me to the research division. That's how I came to work simultaneously in two departments. I was 29. I could run from one place to the other.

Two days a week, after work, I would drive to Flushing near Utopia Parkway to the last stop on the subway into Manhattan. I'd park along the road and take the train to NYU for a two hour lecture. After midnight, I'd take the subway back out to Flushing to get my car. In the winter, when it snowed, I'd have to search out my car, clearing off windshield after windshield until I could find mine. Then I'd make the long drive back to Farmingdale out on the Island, trying to stay awake and on the road. By the time I got home it would be the middle of the night, but often I would read the books I had brought home from school. The next morning I'd be back at work at Central Islip.

Central Islip is a psychiatric hospital. Back in 1959, the range of patients was enormous, from the temporarily depressed to the abused teenager, from the alcoholic to the congenitally deficient nervous system. It was the age of institutional response to human need in New York State. The work load was heavy, but the institutional setting and fury of the madness around me seemed to isolate me from the world in a way that facilitated my need to work long hours alone and feed my own particular madness.

I had only one thing in mind: to do research. It became monolithic and devouring and I loved it. It was a narcotic. It was in my dream state. I read books I never thought I would read and built a chemistry library. This is usual for an academic, but I had never dreamed of becoming an academic.

But more than that, I had to produce.

The facility at Central Islip was built in a park of towering trees and lush grassy fields. Its colonial brick buildings, covered with ivy, reminded me of the University of Pennsylvania. The day I arrived I was greeted on the front steps by a band. One leading three. The conductor waved his arms with feeling. The others all played the same instrument: combs with tissue paper. They were playing "My Country 'Tis of Thee." They buzzed all afternoon. They were pure and sincere.

The dental clinic occupied a full wing of one of the red brick buildings. It was a great open room with massive institutional windows all around. The dental chairs were set near the windows. It was wonderful to look out on all the greenery of the hospital grounds. The view offered a sense of openness and freedom, belied only by thin steel bars befitting a psychiatric hospital. I settled in quickly, being familiar with clinic life in the Navy. My patients, on the other hand, did things that were unfamiliar to me. They cleaned the chair with the edge of their gowns before sitting and asked where my hidden phone was. Sometimes they took off their clothes absentmindedly, and sometimes they brought flowers. Some screamed, some cried. Some punched and cursed. Most were simply appreciative of our care.

The advantage I had, coupled with the ignorance of youth, was this enormous energy. I thought anything was possible. Looking back on it, the combination of ignorance and arrogance was just what got me my first research grant. I had done some work with mice and came to the conclusion that the spontaneous breast tumor of the C3H mouse was easily inhibited by a particular steroid.

Being a graduate student at NYU, I immediately thought in terms of research grants. I made a few phone calls and went right down to the Damon Runyon Memorial Fund in Manhattan. They suggested I speak to my professor at NYU, who just happened to be on the committee for that particular fund. You have to understand that I was completely ignorant of how these things are supposed to be done. I was so excited, I went directly to the school. And not knowing that you had to make an appointment with his secretary, I simply barged in on the great man in his laboratory. There he was, asleep on the top of his chemistry bench, with his head on a little pillow.

I hardly noticed this reclining figure where test tubes and beakers should be. I was bubbling over with arrogance and enthusiasm. I woke him. He sat up, still half asleep, there on his bench. I proceeded to introduce myself and he recognized me from his large lecture class.

He was very embarrassed and a little confused, but I proceeded to ramble on. I ran through all the experiments I had done. He was rubbing his eyes, and trying to figure out who the hell this kid was who had broken into his lab.

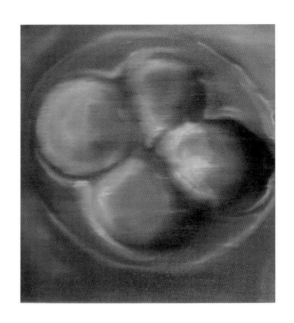

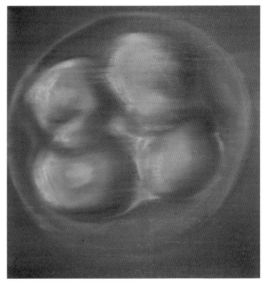

22

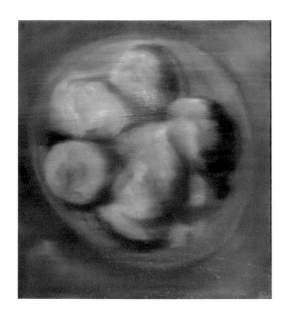

This brief narrative of discovery is as much about the somewhat personal and at times unorthodox ways of thinking that led me to questions concerning the first pulse as it is an explanation of what I found.

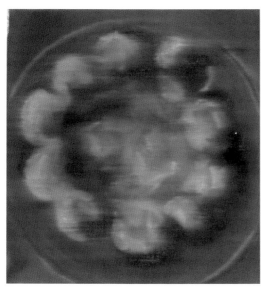

We stood there in silence until he finally said, "Ask for $3,000.00." By the way he said it, I instantly understood we had made an agreement. He would approve the grant, and I wouldn't say anything about him sleeping on his lab bench. He was an austere professor to whom we all owe an intellectual debt. And I'm sure he deserved the sleep I so carelessly interrupted.

He was the head of biochemistry at NYU. He taught fundamentals, which were changing at that time. After I had read his papers I thought he had missed something. He was very interested in the reactivity of membranes and cell interiors and thought he could study them by injecting cells with a microneedle filled with oil and study the refractive forces on that oil. I thought he should have gone straight to chemistry. He gave us our basic information on metabolic cycles and major gene chemistry, the synthesis of nucleic acids and responsiveness of nucleic acid to regulatory substances.

That was in 1959. The first papers on DNA had been published in 1953. He was part of the change over to the study of the nucleic acids. So this was the new way and the new light. It was still fresh and exciting. Lederberg had already done his work on the change in the coats of the bacteria as a function of DNA. We were all pretty much focused on the information transfer residing in that molecule. What was not known was the numerous forces that control the expression of code and that allow it to oscillate between health and disease.

I went back to the State Hospital and began ordering supplies. A few days later I called the Damon Runyon Fund and asked "Where's my check?" And in a couple of days, lo and behold, there was my check. Two more days passed, and I got an embarrassed call from the same administrator from whom I had arrogantly demanded my money. "You didn't fill out an application. You've got to get one to us right away," he said nervously. I had completely forgotten to actually apply.

Meanwhile, the hospital workers were busy building my lab in the basement of the clinic. I located it when I first got there. It was a lovely space, albeit a little hot from the steam pipes. Cages were brought in from other parts of the hospital and mice arrived from Maine. They repaired the old sinks. It had just been storage, but it was convenient because it was directly below the clinic and I could run down between patients. I began breeding mouse colonies.

To keep the animal facility in top shape I engaged the services of a patient. His name was Rufus. He was an animal lover and desperately wanted to work with the mice. He enjoyed feeding them and taking care of them. Rufus didn't have any teeth, so I made him dentures, but he only wore them occasionally. One day I opened the freezer down in the animal room and there were Rufus' teeth. He explained that he liked to put them in the freezer because it helped numb the pain from wearing them. From that day on I counted on Rufus to be imaginative and resourceful.

Rufus hated to see the animals die, as they often did from the spontaneous mammary tumor. Rufus would discover them in the sawdust and try to revive them. I remember coming into the animal room and seeing Rufus with a syringe trying to pump air into the mouth of a mouse that had expired. I let him continue with this rather futile mouse CPR.

Upstairs in the dental clinic, the hospital carpenters built me a cabinet—something like a large telephone booth, closed on three sides. Inside was a four foot square work table, where I had an incubator for cell cultures and an inverted phase Zeiss microscope. My dental chair was in the corner of the vast clinic. To the right, but a little in front of the booth, was my patient, where I could observe him during pauses in treatment. On my roll-about stool I could easily work at the microscope, then move a foot and a half, interview patients, and begin treatment. During the many intervals, such as when anesthesia was taking effect, noncommunicative patients wouldn't mind at all if I moved over and minced tissues or watched cells react to agents. Between patients, I would race down the stairs to my mice. The steam pipes, though wrapped, made it hot. I installed a high speed fan for them, but ran down every hour or two, just in case something went wrong.

I could relate to the patients and to the microscope, study cell cultures and keep my schedule. I could work with small scissors on a glass slab with sterile medium and get a lot of experiments done. I could run downstairs, check on the mice, run back upstairs, wash my hands, and inject a patient. I did this for many years. Almost everyone approved, because it did not interrupt the usual habits of treatment. After work I would carry on uninterrupted for many hours.

Down in the basement I had my mouse colony, which generated, among other things valuable to research, some rather pungent odors. During the summer, would escape the little room and travel up the elevator shaft to the operating room on the top floor. Now the head nurse, doing what she was supposed to do, would smell this, come down to the dental clinic and chew me out appropriately. This happened at least once a week. She'd storm down and say, "How can you have such a thing and make such a smell in a place where human beings are being treated?" And I'd apologize profusely and genuinely and say I was going to go right down and clean the cages again, take out all the refuse, ventilate, and swear it would never happen again. But of course it would happen again, because it was hot down there and the mice often died on the weekend. No matter how hard I tried it still smelled.

Under the microscope I would look up through the bottoms of the dishes at cell lines extracted from my mice. I studied the effects of various substances on various mammalian cells, preparing them downstairs where I had chemicals and a balance. I would weigh them out and heat them if neces-

We have to understand energy flow to understand anything in science. Information storage and transfer and energy storage and transfer are the dynamics of nature and biology.

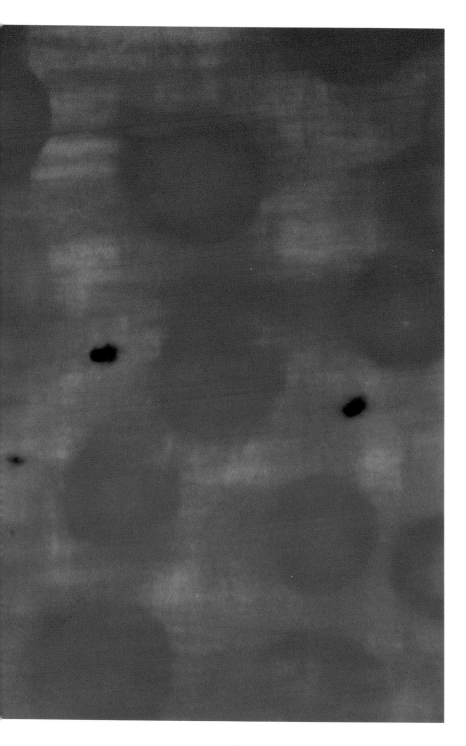

sary, adjust the pH, bottle them, and run up the stairs with a syringe. I looked at all the carbohydrates, the fatty acids, the amino acids, and the vitamins. I studied the effects of the common essential mineral salts on cell growth. I also found an old pond which grew enough slime to supply me with algae and protozoa. I grew things and added substances that would hopefully modify growth in some way that would give me an idea of patterns and nutritive forces. What were the metabolic forces, and what were the inhibitory forces?

I had learned about chemical inhibitors, such as fluoride, iodo-acetate, azide, and dinitro-phenol, as well as all the common agents used to map out the metabolic pathways at NYU. I used whatever was around. If there were good soluble drugs around or chemotherapy agents, I dumped them in. Still, I was beginning to develop a healthy bias. One of the interesting things about the mineral corticoids, I had begun working with through the Damon Runyon Fund grant, was that they were relatively non-toxic. So I had already made non-toxicity a priority, even though most of the cancer cell inhibitors commonly in use were anything but.

There were between six and eight thousand patients at the State Hospital at any given time. People came in with bumps and lumps and gashes. They had weird rashes and swellings of every kind. I even saw oral tuberculosis, which had disappeared in the general population. There were more diagnostic events than I had ever experienced before, even in the Navy. I saw a lot more oral cancer at the State Hospital, more than I could have seen anywhere else. Lots of rubbery-red carcinomas of the tongue and cheek lining and a great number of tumors of the salivary glands.

One thing we saw at the State Hospital that you never saw anywhere else was what was known as *proud flesh*. Proud flesh was common in the First World War before the development of antibiotics. Left unattended and unsutured, the middle of the wound grows up like red rubber. It looks like carcinoma. If you have clinical experience you get scared because these things are big and grow fast. So you send it around to all the other clinics to get it biopsied and get opinions. You have the wound irrigated, but the psychiatric patient won't let you stitch it. It's very much like someone in the trenches that no medic could get to. Then something amazing happens. After ten or twelve days of concern, it gets pale and contracts. In just a few more days, it's down to a tiny ugly scar and it's gone. What has happened is that the circulation, energy, and nutrition has reached it. The growth factors have poured into this granulation tissue.

Proud flesh is an example of the reversibility of the anaerobic state, the oxygen deprived state.

Otto Warburg, the brilliant German scientist, had discovered that tumors were oxygen deficient 30 years before. Warburg's great work *Auf Stoffwechsel der Tumoren* (*On the Mechanism of Cancer*), had never been translated into English. I read it with an English/German dictionary. Translating word by word, I realized that aerobic oxidation was deficient in cancer, and I found it fascinating. And this old question led to hundreds of other questions which form the story of my research up until now–of the experiments required to study the differences in cells at the gene level that have different metabolic systems and energies.

As time went on I realized that organisms must have different gene expressions during different states of stress, such as dehydration, or starvation, heat shock or chemical shock, even allergic challenge. When there is an energy deficit the energy expression must be adequate for the gene expression. Cells in turn have evolved to select the particular routes of gene reaction which work together. These responses by the cell allow it to function with particular groups of genes and enzymes. These serve the stress and the challenge and do not expend energy in the usual pathways, but conserve energy to meet this particular problem when the battery runs low. The system either shuts down or follows a different information pathway, a diabolically sophisticated choice. The transcription of genes, the translation of genes, was routinely, rapidly shifted to different kinds of expression and the cell assumed different states. So when we speak of cancer as an anaerobic model, or something without air, we are speaking of a system that makes use of available glucose, the cell's source of energy, in the most efficient way, but does not expend the energy at the same rate. It does not produce the same shared synthetic products, the same membrane products. This anaerobic state is embryonic. It survives by a particular budgeting of the glucose reaction. The lower energy state suggested models of treatment based upon changing the metabolic signal, changing the energy signals to normalize for the stress, to modify and select the anaerobic into the aerobic. This theory kept me occupied for thirty years.

The deformity of proud flesh was modest compared to that of the tumor. The tumor is much more deprived of the aerobic force of the intrinsic enzymes in the cell that allow aerobic metabolism to return. But in a way, cancer is that incurable wound. So to cure the wound, the anaerobic wound, we had to go further. We had to define the original enzymatic gene site events which converted the anaerobic to the aerobic. We had to define the groups of enzymes that came in early and allowed oxygen to be available.

Not long after I arrived at Central Islip I met Jack Heyman, who was the senior research chemist at the hospital working on neurological biochemistry, studying schizophrenia. Jack came to the Research Division to do research on drugs that would help the mentally ill. It required an enormous number of disciplines to focus on those problems.

Within the division was a biochemistry section that was involved in basic science. I fit well there, because I too was doing basic science. The major responsibility of the biochemistry laboratory was to study the new pharmacoactive agents and see how they effected metabolism. There were about six people working there. They did critical assays on serum and urine and had their own conferences and visiting scholars.

Jack was a young and enthusiastic researcher and was able to convey to me the excitement of molecular mechanisms and molecular personalities; that chemistry wasn't simple, but rather magical and wonderful. And if you worked in an area, you could actually discover things that were unique to it. Therefore, you could actually make discoveries, because the context for chemistry is larger than you could ever imagine. So if you work in a little corner of chemistry you might wind up with a tremendous story about how those chemicals interact. He conveyed by personality and enthusiasm that chemical kinetics was indeed a fascinating thing to look at. It is a description of life. You can uncover, in the microform, some magic which, when followed, produces a web of relationships which connects you to everything in the world. Molecules are wonderful and have personalities.

Jack was a thoughtful man and a well trained biochemist, capable of thinking chemically and metabolically, all the while trying to formulate something neurologic and chemical to explain and to help the patients. We were instant friends. He would take me over to his house for lunch with his family. He was more senior, more advanced, so he could critique my work and give me advice. It was science, unalloyed with no axes to grind, that brought us together. We were both interested in the unknown. We had faith that laboratory methods would reveal secrets just beneath the surface.

When I had something happen, I would call him immediately and he would do further research, checking the literature. Then he'd be by in an hour or so. I would say "How can this be?" and he would say, "Well, I can think of a few ways. You could promote it this way, or block it that way." Chemists have the knowledge of pathways, and I began to realize that a chemist not only believes that anything is possible but that it can be done in many different ways.

At the time I was studying intermediate metabolites, which is very relevant to fundamental influences. We designed rather broad-based experiments at the level of biochemistry and genetics. We did Warburg fermentation studies and the effects on bacteria and tumor cells in the big tanks.

It was a very interesting apparatus. Today there are simpler methods that are less mechanically complex. Back then you had a large stainless steel tank—a water bath. A dozen glass flasks were arranged around the perimeter of the tank, then inserted in the water bath. Each of these flasks had a manometer tube that read the barometric pressure of the gas within the flask. Cells and culture media were put in the flask along with the test substance. In the side arm of the flask we put a blotter paper that was wet with potassium

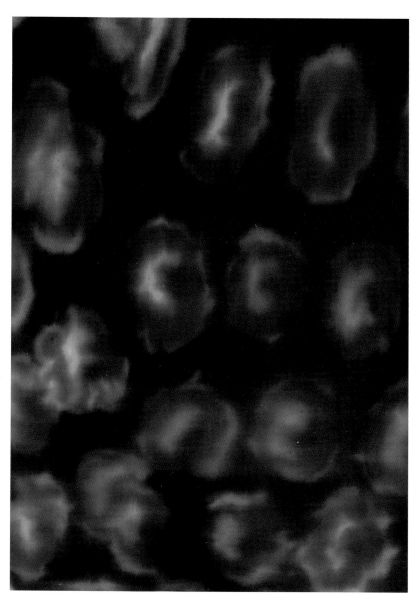

At that moment on a winter day in 1955, something happened that touched my inner being. I had recognized something in that visualization of the cancer cell which identified the disease as something that could be understood viscerally from the inside out.

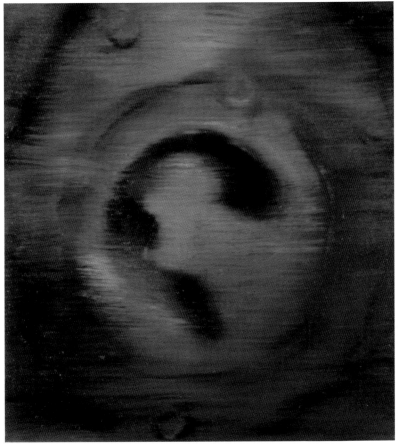

Dense chromatin in the nucleus of the cell.

But in a way, cancer is that incurable wound. So to cure the wound, the anaerobic wound, we had to go further.

hydroxide solution to take up the carbon dioxide that was produced. In this way the manometer reading would more or less reflect the utilization of oxygen. The whole apparatus had to shake and oscillate in the water bath to stir the contents continually and equilibrate or make even the temperature of all the flasks and their contents.

This thing would shake, rattle, and roll, and some of the flasks would break and fall into the water bath. It took hours to set up, a day to run, and a day to break down and clean up. While it was running, there were at least two people trying to read the manometers while the thing was shaking.

There was an enormous amount of data: we ran these experiments for years on a whole variety of substances that had to do with pharmacological agents that affect the psyche, for the management of mental patients. We also ran test substances to explore the theoretical responses of the biochemical schemes within the cells. The studies involved not only defined substances, but fractions from serum taken from patients in an attempt to understand schizophrenia.

We gathered data on expected pathway responses and a knowledge of which agents promoted or inhibited metabolism. I learned my trade from active measurements on biological responses that read out in oxygen utilization data. Depending on how you designed your experiments the data could be quite complicated in terms of the chemistry in the individual substances. Jack and I worked together until he went to Ohio State to work for Chemical Abstract Services.

It took me twenty-six years to begin to understand these pathways. And all the way there was the search for effective, efficient, safe compounds. The little discoveries along the way led to yet other questions in an imperceptibly slow movement toward something not yet known, like time lapse photography. There were uncountable cultures to assay, and innumerable compounds to make.

On Mondays I'd come in to find out who in my mouse colony had died over the weekend. Digging them out of the sawdust I would begin the grim task of dissecting the ripe little animals to see if the compounds had any effect on the tumors, what kinds of cell necrosis I had produced, or conversely, if the tumor had spread. It was a gruesome, but necessary procedure, since the mouse had often been dead for days. Such was my life at the clinic. Still there was no question that I would some day find a successful therapy, though I wouldn't want to have to do it again. After I was done with the tests, Rufus would bury the little creatures behind the old building.

Each morning, I would arrive to a greeting from one of our permanent residents. He would yell out "PHARAOH," extending the last syllable like an auctioneer. Around noon, the head of my department would crawl up into the fetal position on the wide ledge under the big barred windows and scream at the top of his lungs in some kind of home grown primal therapy. And at the end of the day, I'd sit there at the microscope with most of the lights out. The low sunlight would come in through the venetian blinds and throw slats of light across the floor, and into my cubicle. Then the patients upstairs would start to pee out their windows. At the same time every evening, the urine would run down the tall institutional windows, and the whole place would be awash in undulating shimmering yellow light.

2. A Change of Course

I had been lucky during my early years in research. I was going through steroids just to find the range of interaction and I found steroids that made tumors grow and steroids that inhibited growth. Several others found the same results and published before I did. But it was exciting, and it let me know that this disease could be slowed in a relatively non-toxic way. This was around 1961 and it left me with the burning question of how to do it better and what was next?

Every cancer researcher thinks on the cellular level right from the beginning, because the cell is the fundamental biological unit. But poisoning the gene material didn't seem to have a theoretical base. It seemed to be a floundering, random position that institutions took because they had nothing else. By 1965 everybody was looking for the magic bullet in the rain forests and at the bottom of the sea. But this search was based on an incomplete scientific position. Understanding the normal was what was needed. And understanding, as I saw it, would have to be directed at cell development. I would need to know what a cell was, and how I was going to approach the magnitude of the problem. And the problem was much more intricate than anyone had thought. I needed a new context to talk about the unknown, to let the context emerge by suspending habits. I had to train myself to look and listen by refusing to set up a rigid system to define the unknown.

The old thinking was to poison the gene material, since the cancer cell was mean and savage. Now life is cruel, but the molecular events in it are neutral. There's no malice in a tumor. It is we who have resentments and anger and grief. The tumor is neutral, there's simply nobody at the desk. So I thought I might as well find out how this thing was put together. It was at that point that I determined to restore the normal, rather than poison the abnormal.

I always knew there would have to be a departure from the poison of the month club. I was looking for a pathway, something that operated then dropped out. I wanted to restore the cell. I went through a long series of remarkably successful experiments to find and localize the pathway. I eventually discovered respiratory substrates which caused inhibition in the tumor cell. These substances were natural metabolites found in living organisms, which contributed to the mitochondrial reactions, the aerobic oxidation pathways referred to in the Krebs citric acid cycle.

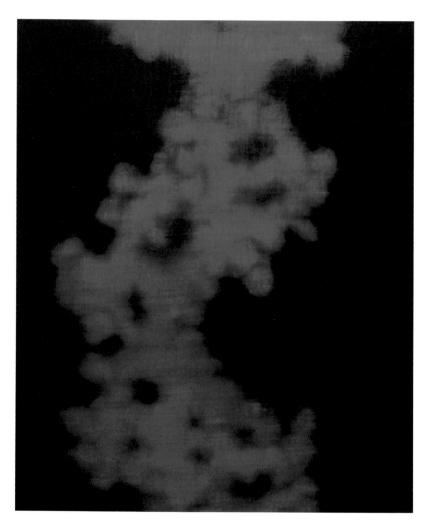

Poisoning the gene material didn't seem to have a theoreti-
cal base. It seemed to be a floundering, random position that
institutions took because they had nothing else.

There are ten enzyme steps which are circular in this basic metabolic cycle within the normal cell. These enzymes take lactic acid, the residue from fermentation, then convert it to pyruvate, circulating it in a series of reactions until it's all converted to carbon dioxide and water. This is in normal tissue that lives and breathes. In order to produce carbon dioxide and water and energy, the little carbon compounds that have come away from fermentation go round and round in the Krebs citric cycle. Within that cycle little organic derivatives we call carboxylic acids are formed. They're all very specific.

One can take these, as I did, and put very large quantities of them into cell cultures. One of the interesting things I found was that there are effects that cause changes in the form of the tumor. They're too weak and are used up too quickly to be an effective therapy, but by putting in massive quantities I could change the shape of the nucleus. I could produce small dense portions in it, which were condensations of the DNA, referred to as dense chromatin or heterochromatin. These are changes in the direction of normality, because if one views, for example, the cells of the lining of the mouth, the nucleus—the dot at the center of the cell—is small and compact. But if you look at a typical tumor cell it has a great big nucleus that's not dense at all. I was on the right track.

I had found four molecules that caused dense chromatin: the neutral salts of malic acid, succinic acid, betahydroxybutyric acid and alphaglycero phosphoric acid. The results were visual and I could measure them optically. There was definitely a change in the state at the gene level, not adequately described, though heavily studied. That density was what I was interested in. I tried to reproduce it. There was a sense that it was restorative, even though it was small, incomplete, and ineffective as therapy. But it confirmed my hunch that you could get into the nucleus without killing it.

What I did was photograph the cancer cell with a video camera (then called a "vidicon") through a microscope, then put the microscopic image up on the monitor. I attached a light meter to the end of a cardboard tube which was the diameter of the image of the nucleus, then read the light density which was changing as a function of the concentration of the reagent I was adding. Then I plotted the increase in density readings. On the screen you'd see lots of dark dots in the nucleus of the cancer cells. Those darker dots symbolized the direction toward the normal.

About that time I found that much to my surprise there was a new cancer research facility, working on federal grants, called the Waldemar Foundation, in Woodbury, Long Island. I usually had to go into New York for that kind of thing. So I called them up and they said, "Hey that's interesting, you're doing cancer research at the State Hospital. We're looking for ways to grow. Come out and see us." So I did. The first day the Director, Dr.

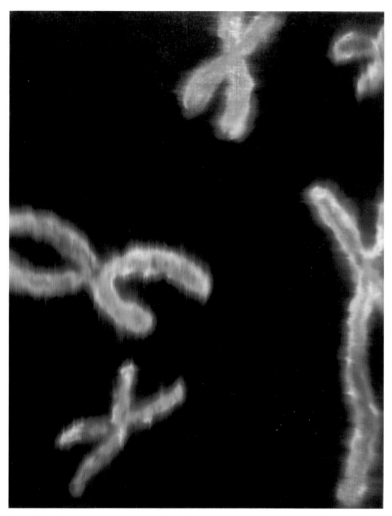

By 1965 everybody was looking for the magic bullet in the rain forests and at the bottom of the sea.

Norman Molomut, said, "Let's get you some space, and get you started. We all need each other."

It was a two story building set in the side of a hill. The ground floor was all animal facilities. Upstairs were the chemistry labs, the biology laboratories, the biophysics laboratories, and the administration. There was also a conference room and library. We usually ate lunch together in the conference room. There was no gap between the students and the teachers. The Director's door was always open, since they prided themselves on the fact

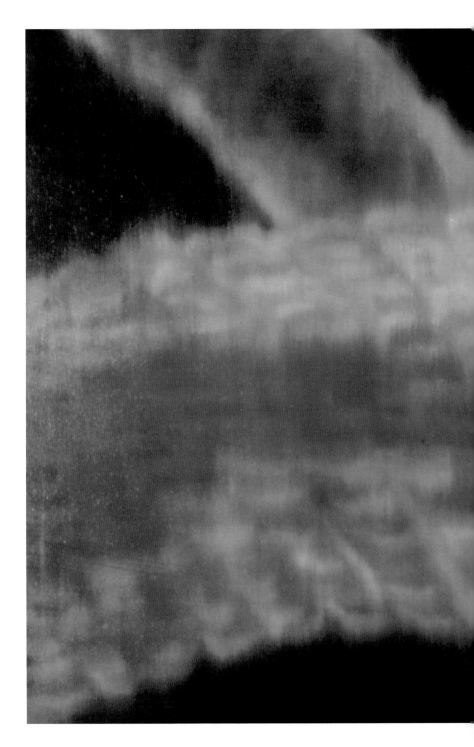

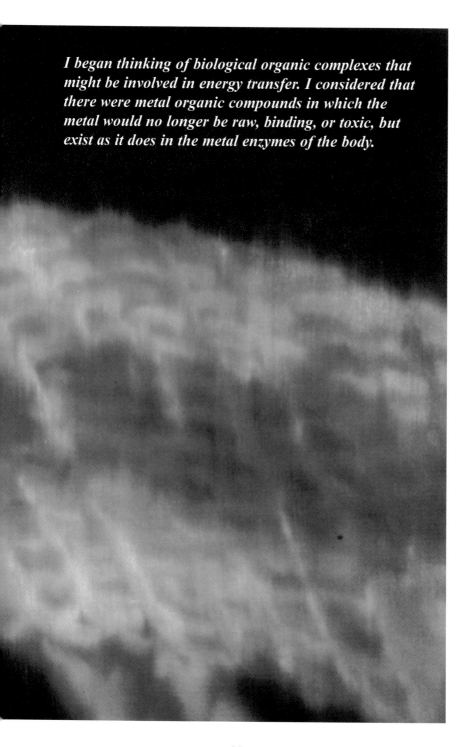

I began thinking of biological organic complexes that might be involved in energy transfer. I considered that there were metal organic compounds in which the metal would no longer be raw, binding, or toxic, but exist as it does in the metal enzymes of the body.

that anyone could walk in without an appointment and talk to Dr. Molomut. The staff also included Dr Morty Padnos, a virologist from NYU, and Dr. Margaret MacDonald, a biochemist who came from Cold Spring Harbor at the inception of the institution. They gave me a nice space downstairs at the animal room level and helped me with equipment and supplies.

It was a small cancer research facility with a fine laboratory, a talented staff with well-trained technicians and support staff, and integrated communications. It had good ties to the community for fund raising, and they were familiar with the roots of federal financing and grant support, especially to the National Science Foundation.

There was a virology group studying viruses that grow in tumors and can destroy some of them. There were people doing extracts from tissue, and isolating enzymes that act on RNA and DNA. There were biophysicists devising new instrumentation to use in the laboratory, including optical methods. There were teaching programs for the design of curricula for the training of young scientists which was federally supported. And there was a vast summer program of visiting scientists and students. It had a full-time staff of around 40 people.

They had exceptional animal facilities for the study of cancer. They had standard inbred strains of mice and rats, and standard cell lines that they cultivated in the mice and rats which were suitable for screening drugs. They taught the techniques of handling the animals and culturing and transplanting the cells. There was a long-term study on the effect of magnetic fields on growth and malignant growth. There were also graduate students from Hofstra and Adelphi Universities who did their graduate work at Waldemar in degree programs.

During those years, I worked in both the Hospital and at Waldemar. It was only ten exits down the expressway from Central Islip. At lunch or when I had a large project underway, I could race down the highway at 70 mph and be at Waldemar in a matter of minutes.

I learned many techniques in cell culture and screening with animals. I learned biochemical methods relating to genetics and examination of nucleic acids. We also did some chemistry on the dense chromatin I had caused with the respiratory substrates.

I was using a very large cell culture in a complex chamber in which one thin film extended under the microscope, and the rest of the culture, which was as much as 20 cc, had a calcium electrode emersed in the media while the media was being stirred with a magnetic stirrer. We read the calcium concentration in the media as a response to the drug uptake. It showed that the substrates were bringing calcium into the tumor cells. Then we extracted the DNA from the tumor cells and isolated the DNA without displacing the mineral salts associated with it. We didn't use strong acid, but a detergent method and alcohol and we recovered the calcium. I showed that the ratio of calcium increased at the DNA level as a response to these substrates.

When I took the DNA out of the Ehrlich tumor line that had been treated with sodium malate, I found that the amount of calcium associated with the DNA had increased, so that one aspect of the inhibition was the uptake in calcium. The other thing was that malate was an electron donor. The hydrogen that came off went to the electron transport chain. Therefore, the two mechanisms that emerged from the dense chromatin experiments were electron transfer and calcium uptake.

Calcium is a major regulator. If it gets too high it's toxic. It links a great many proteins and can bind to DNA. There's a normal tolerable concentration of calcium that's supposed to be in the cell. Variations from that level are pathological. Since I could monkey with that using calcium carriers, which are natural substrates, there was a possibility for a therapeutic approach. However, it seemed to have limits. From our vantage point today, I can see that we probably displaced a proton from DNA and put a calcium on it. And that has a configurational influence. It's just that I was able to do something at that end of the metabolic scheme.

I was interested in both calcium transfer and electron transfer. But I believed in electron transfer more, because I felt that it was related to energies that would manipulate ions like calcium. It was something to be looked at, because it told me that respiratory metabolism could be restored. It was a direction that could modify and select toward therapy. So I thought, there's a way to get there, but I have to carry on this reaction in a continuum so that a lot of energy or a lot of that exchange continues to go on, in a prolonged and rapid way. Metallo-organic compounds seemed the most promising.

The first metallo-organics that showed influence were cobalt compounds. I published a paper in 1969 on the electrogenic effect of a synthetic oxygen carrying cobalt compound. Back at the State Hospital I was doing electroencephalographic readings on mice injected with anti-tumor agents, because I understood that it was an electrical event. I had been reading from Martel & Calvin's work *Metal Chelation*. These were scientists who had explored photosynthesis. I departed from the existing recipes by changing the ligands, the organic part of the compound. At the time I probably had made 20 or 30 cobalt compounds. One caused seizures in the mice, so I thought, let's look at it on the EEG.

Since I worked in a psychiatric hospital, there was an EEG clinic nearby and the staff was amenable to my running animals on machines meant for humans. I took my mice over to the EEG center, hooked them up to the electrodes and put them on a little metal plate in a drawer. They sat surprisingly still in the dark.

We'd run a base line on the EEG, then I'd give them the drug. I was interested in toxicity and whether there were seizure discharges. Now the mouse showed seizure potentials like a human, and we had a supervisor there that no one liked. He would come in and look over our shoulders and here would be these tracings of a Jacksonian Epilepsy and he'd say, "What do you have, a signal generator?" and we'd say "No, a patient." He'd look around through the glass windows, trying to see the patient. Then he would go out in the hall, and look up and down, scratching his head, because none of the patients were hooked up to the machine. He'd walk back in and the seizure tracing would be going mad, spraying ink all over everything.

We never told him and he never knew we had a mouse in the drawer. The cobalt was discharging a tremendous amount of stored energy in the brain. After the tests the mice always recovered completely. At the time I wasn't interested in studying epilepsy, though I had produced Jackson seizures. With the help of my associates at Waldemar, I published a paper, because I thought it might serve as a model for those studying epilepsy.

In the spring of 1969 I attended a lecture at NYU given by George Fried. He was the best lecturer I'd heard at NYU. George was dynamic and interesting and he understood metabolism, especially fat metabolism. He had the material at his fingertips. He didn't use notes. I was impressed. I went to his lab at Beth Israel Hospital and began to talk with him. It was a big biochemistry lab with benches, hoods, glassware, Keldahl apparatus, a centrifuge, things that heat, filter, and isolate. He was studying rats and recovering glycerol phosphate dehydrogenase enzyme from their tissues and measuring the enzymes spectrally.

Shortly after that he took me to Brooklyn College with him and created an advanced study course for me on the literature of biological electron transport. Naturally, the different electron transfers in tumors was a major subject. I read the original Warburg again to try to understand the meaning of atmungsferment. I did some protozoa studies there as well.

George gave me a room where I set up my microscope so that we could study dense chromatin and its relation to electron transfer. I was studying the substrate, and he was studying the enzyme that acted on it, so it was a natural merger. George thought it had something to do with fat metabolism. I thought it had something to do with electron transfer. We were both correct. We had no conflict. We really wanted to talk about why these things should be regulatory. Why they should be controlling. And we both wanted to read the electron transfer literature. The good part was hanging out with George. The bad part was the lack of parking near the Brooklyn College campus. We'd stay in the building until 2:00 in the morning, then we'd go out on Flatbush Avenue and eat at one of the all night diners. We'd pig-out and talk until the early morning.

We studied fat metabolism, isoenzymes, and we searched for an explanation of the metabolic pathways for obesity. We studied the cell membrane. There are

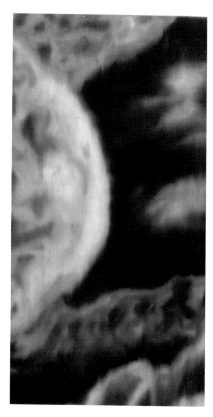

For some reason I was a very good cook in this area. I don't know why, but I had no trouble at all in dreaming up compounds. It was a madness of cooking day and night, a frenzy of work through many nights.

wet groups, phosphor groups, and polar groups tied to the fatty acids that allow them to communicate in a very controlled way with other substances like proteins which are wet. You have the problems in emerging cellular systems in dealing with substances that are oil soluble and substances that are water soluble. So you have emulsoid interfaces and you have ways of transferring information across them, across this phase boundary in which oil and water regulate and partly separate, but do not completely separate the compartments of the cell from each other or the external world from the cell. This emulsoid stage is pretty fascinating and if you disrupt it severely you'll have pretty toxic events and seizure potentials, but it is possible to transfer across them.

The literature on electron transfer that I studied at Brooklyn College had nothing in it about the physical biochemistry. There was only the reaction pathways, the mitochondria, cytochromes, the flavo proteins, the particles, and the number of ATP produced per unit of oxygen, as well as the P:O ratios, the amount of sugar, the differences between poisoned systems that are blocked and unpoisoned, coupled and uncoupled, anaerobic and aerobic. All that is information about electron transfer which is descriptive enzymatics, but not physical biochemistry.

Studying the literature did give me confidence that there was an event here that required pure physical chemistry and that it should be separated out from biochemistry which observed the event of the electron transfer and its presence or absence. I felt that I had a grasp of the literature, but that the ability to manipulate electron transfer resided in compounds I didn't have at my disposal. These were industrial-type compounds containing metals. I

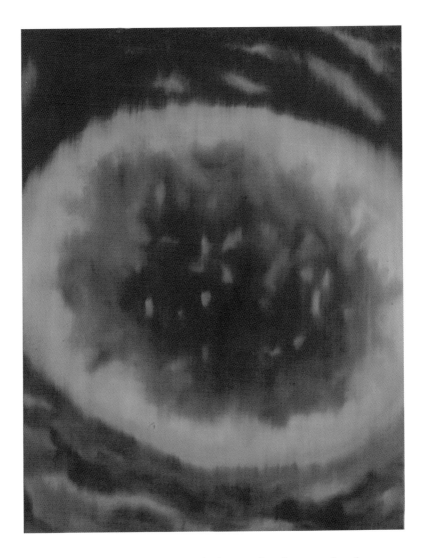

I had determined that I needed to make thousands of compounds for the particular research I had set out to do. I spent thirteen years on vanadium. Vanadium makes wonderful compounds. Someday someone will cure diabetes with it.

came to believe that metals were the catalyst of electron transfer. I would have to study metals and metallo-organic chemistry. Because of this realization, I became very interested in electrochemistry as an analytic method to study energy transfer in the cell.

And then I realized that I wasn't going to find what I was looking for in the organic chemistry literature, and I had the wrong instruments. I wanted to look at these things and measure them, but I didn't want to use spectroscopy, because it didn't give me the information I was looking for.

If I was going to measure electron transfer, I needed to talk about electronics rather than electrons. I needed to learn how the cell was wired. And in order to learn the electronics of the cell, I had to study electrochemistry and corrosion engineering, which led me to instruments such as the polarograph. I believed that there was electronics to be looked at and that the electronics was in the catalyst and in the cell and somehow they were related. There was cell circuitry to study.

I obtained the equipment and began to do charge transfer polarography on a whole variety of materials. There was a convergence of the technical and the idea. It seemed that the compounds I was looking for were industrial-type compounds containing metals, so I began working on biological catalysts in which there was an organic molecule bonded to a *d* transition metal.

Now if you start studying electron transfer, or hydrogenation, most of the literature deals with industrial catalytic reactions, such as petroleum cracking, which involves high heat without oxygen in the presence of metals in a solid surface form or in a bed or matrix to which the liquids or gases are forced. The metal surface or the metal itself has electrical properties like nothing else in nature. What metals do is share electrons on a very extended leash, a geometric form we call the *d* electron, visualized as a very long tear drop, the point of which is at the atomic center. Their electrons not only overlap with each other, as in conductivity in a wire or metal structures, but they expand into solvents and interact with organic molecules dispersed in those solvents.

I began thinking of biological organic complexes that might be involved in energy transfer. I considered that there were metal organic compounds in which the metal would no longer be raw, binding, or toxic, but would exist as it does in the metal enzymes of the body. I was fortunate to meet people who were more advanced than I was—scholars in the study of metal enzymes. It was about that time that I began working with molybdenum. Molybdenum compounds were more exciting, more sophisticated, subtler, and more difficult to coordinate and define than any metal I had worked with.

Ed Steifel was the most influential of my teachers. I was working on molybdenum compounds at Waldemar around 1974 and Ed Steifel, who was a professor of chemistry at Stony Brook, called me out of nowhere and said he'd heard I was working with molybdenum and that we were the only two people on the East Coast working with it. I never asked him how he found out. I went out to Stony Brook and sat in on his course and stayed for 2-1/2 years.

Stony Brook had a Chemtrix polaragraph. Ed also had an Electron Spin Resonance Spectrometer. He was running my samples and trying to understand fundamental problems in molecular coordination. We started testing my compounds, interacting an electrical signal with the substrates.

You interact a signal with one material, then add a second to see if it takes from or gives charge to the first. When you first do it you're lost. You've got a lot of wiggley lines. Seeing a reverse curve is always disturbing to someone who is used to working with the forward curve of sine waves. Suddenly you have a forward curve on top and a reverse curve on the bottom. It's a cycle. The pen is going forward and back. You run a voltage ramp up to a volt and then back to zero. It's adding charge, then it's pulling it out. First you add electrons, then you pull them back. Like making a bank deposit followed by an immediate withdrawal, only with electrons instead of cash. That's a cyclic scan.

We made compounds and talked about the synergic relationship between metals and organics. Applications were there, but it was a question of attitude, whether one has a stronger feeling about the chemicals or the applications. I became familiar with the fundamental reactions, the kinetics and structures. Ed in turn was happy to learn about applications. We started at opposite places and met in the middle.

He spent a lot of time on molybdenum, but was particularly interested in nitrogenases, the mysterious enzymes that pull nitrogen out of the air as with alfalfa and other related rhizome type vegetables or plants. There is a particular bacterium in the roots of these vegetations which, in concert with the root, can pull the nitrogen out at the vaporous stage and convert it to nitrates. It's a molybdenum enzyme and it also has iron in it. It's one of the challenges that many large corporations wanted to understand. They thought perhaps that they could feed plants air—gaseous nitrogen—rather than filling the soil with nitrate salts, so a great deal of money was spent studying nitrogenase. It turns out that this is one of the most complex catalytic structures in the universe, not likely to ever be synthesized. It also turns out that there is vanadium nitrogenase as well as molybdenum nitrogenase, which shows as any chemist knows that you can always do it in another way and, possibly, in a more efficient way.

I made lots of molybdenum compounds, and they have therapeutic uses. The most efficient were sandwiches which means that there is a metal sandwiched between two organics. It's interesting if one of the organics is white bread and one is rye, so to speak. So it's an asymmetric sandwich which means that the energy flow can be from one of the organics through the metal into the other organic. What we have is a liquid transistor. We've found that you can refine electronics in liquids just as you do in a radio or television, providing your wave forms and your electronics are well modulated. We had to learn to tune our molecules.

Molybdenum had some promise of cancer therapy in it. It was incomplete, however. I had an awful lot of molybdenum compounds that were promising, but never quite fulfilled the potency we needed. They were a safe, but partial treatment.

When Ed left for Sloan Kettering in Ohio, in 1974, he said, "You know, you ought to take a look at vanadium." Klaus Schwartz had just published a paper that said vanadium is an essential mineral. Its coordination is very similar to molybdenum and it's in a right diagonal descent in the periodic table to molybdenum. A metal with the same diagonal often has similar crystal symmetries. Metals that share the same descending link to the right often have similar reactions in forming compounds in the sense that they interact with similar organic groups or ligands. They form structures and often have similar crystal symmetry. So if we're looking for a group of compounds in coordination, there are traditional relationships in the periodic table that are vertical and horizontal. We must also be aware that there are diagonal relationships. Since it was said to be an essential mineral, I began to look at vanadium. I spent thirteen years on vanadium. Vanadium makes wonderful compounds. Someday someone will cure diabetes with it. There is some connection with sugar transport and some interaction with insulin.

When a molecule loses an electron that's called oxidation, when it takes on an electron that is called reduction. Vanadium has very clear oxidation states. Every time it gives off an electron it changes color, so that just by looking at it you know what its state is and what's hooked to it and how many electrons there are. It's a dream for teaching chemistry. You don't need instruments, you just need your eyes, and your thoughts. It goes from red to orange to yellow to green to blue to indigo to violet to clear. Green is the three state, blue is the four state, and violet is the five state. Those are the number of electrons given up to long distance sharing. It's given them up but it still holds onto them. It keeps them on a long leash. I learned more about metal coordination studying vanadium than anything else.

Vanadium was not only promising, it was hypnotic. With vanadium complexes you get very close to therapy with tumor systems. Vanadium can turn from green to blue and then back to green, which means it has taken an electron and given it back. It's an electron broker, and that's what I was looking for. I always had compounds, though, with very high toxicity. And though you could work with these compounds they were somewhat similar to conventional chemotherapy and I could not break through into a new realm.

The closest thing we had was a compound the National Cancer Institute was interested in, which was a vanadium porphyrin; a beautiful violet compound. This one was the best of all. I thought I was going to go far with this compound. Then I realized, after three or four months, that it crystallizes in the bottle, falls out of solution and you have rather pretty but useless solids at the bottom of a clear solution.

I went through a period of struggle with the porphyrins and, much to my disappointment, the best structures were the ones that tended to fall out of solution after three months. These were the ones that had the most anti-tumor activity. So eventually I went on to other metals, moving further to the right on the periodic table. The important thing was to learn with vanadium and leave it and go elsewhere. It was important for me to stop my vanadium research, but it was very difficult because it had so much promise.

While working with vanadium I did find that you could work in water and that the body probably worked in water most of the time rather than solvents, like acetone, hexane, or pentane. The point is that organic chemists usually work with solvents to make things, but they are inconvenient and toxic. It's necessary to do a lot of solvent syntheses in chemistry, but I learned you could do a lot of chemistry in water. So I thought, let's stay with water, because the body works mostly in water, even though it may work with phases which have no water. There's an enormous amount of water chemistry. So I began to make compounds in water with heat at various pH's. I made thousands of compounds. It was a madness of cooking day and night, a frenzy of work through many nights.

For some reason I was a very good cook in this area. I don't know why, but I had no trouble at all in dreaming up compounds that might be catalytic. The biochemical maps were simple and clear. I could recall ligands that might coordinate to a particular metal, amines or porphorins or sulphurs or whatever was needed to bind that metal. I knew the functional groups and picked as biological models, groups that would be involved in electron transfer. Electron transfer became the technology of the laboratory, and electron transfer measurements became terribly important.

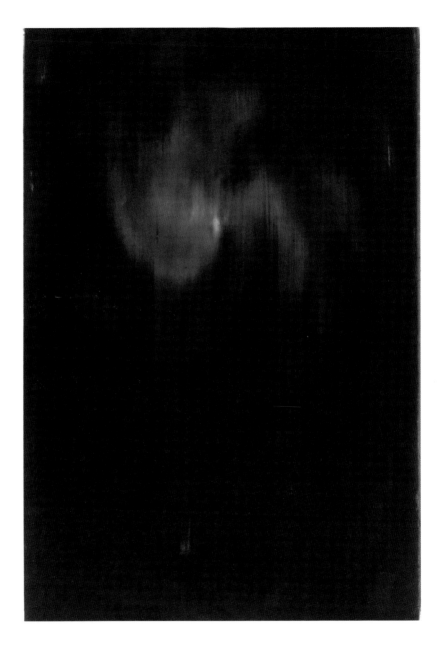

We are an open window to nature. We typically see the organism as a defined entity. But we are fashioned of the universe, and the universe streams through us.

3. Get Down in the Hole and Dig

By 1969 I had moved to another building at the State hospital. I had a table built; a 4 by 8-foot sheet of plywood with an 18-inch high wall around three sides and shelving for the hundreds of the bottles I had acquired.

I needed to make thousands of compounds for the particular work I had set out to do. I needed small glassware, a very simple system for heating them, and an enormous number of reagents (reacting chemicals) close at hand. I kept in mind that all of these reagents were potentially useful. I needed to be sitting because of the long hours necessary to do the work. I had a balance that was small, accurate, and quick, and many small beakers so I could make as many compounds as possible in a given time frame. I believed that it was important to work at this micro level so that my production and screening of compounds would be large in number at the early stages of the search. I thought about how to approach the problem and then did the experiment immediately. I didn't keep mice there; only a few at home in my own basement. I had a baby bottle warmer to sterilize small beakers on the table next to my balance. Very often I'd have to leave to give treatment to patients, and the nice thing about a baby bottle warmer is when it boils out it shuts off. It was an extremely valuable instrument.

Let's say I wanted to make manganese compounds. I wanted to make at least 50. So I'd gather a lot of small beakers, get all my alkali and acid in small dropper bottles at, say, a tenth molar solution, then calculate, measure, mix, and cook, because I couldn't afford to be walking around with a 400 ml beaker, moving from one side of a counter to the other. There's a simple human movement equation to turning out work.

I wanted to combine every transition metal available as a soluble salt with the 22 amino acids, a dozen vitamins, assorted starches, eight nucleotides, and 50 to one hundred intermediate metabolites. Therefore I had quite a few thousand compounds to make. It was daunting, but I could see it. I could see that I had to go through many metals in many combinations, because I believed that the body did it in the blood, in water and not in solvents. I worked at pH 7.4, the serum pH, or as does the cell at pH 5.5.

I'd think, "I'm going to sandwich this metal between this amino acid and this vitamin and it's going to have to go on this one first because it's a ring, and it's going to be sterically shielded, and I'll try to put a small ligand in after that to alter the total oxidation state," and so on. "I'm going to make a mental structure of the molecule, derived from what I've read, from published papers."

Let's say there are two papers published about a compound each describing a different structure. But I know both chemists made compounds. Let's say one thought the metal is floating in the middle of a ring and the other thought the metal was stuck on a nitrogen. But I'm not going to worry about that because it might have been stuck on a nitrogen as a transition state before it got into the middle of the ring. Very often in science when people disagree they're both correct. I always assumed that everyone had a contribution to make.

I wanted to find the molecule before going ahead and refining the structure. That can be done later. If you structure it geometrically, and are too firm, you may never get to make it. The variety of geometries is great, so you do have to know a little bit about crystal structure or crystal field symmetry to imagine what will hook up with what else—whether their shapes will fit together. But in the end it may not matter because you'll vary the recipe by trial and error.

What I wanted to do was synthesize thousands of chemical compounds, first checking for preliminary chemical identity, such as spectral character, then screen them biologically. If it stood up under screening I would then begin structural analysis.

In this way I began to search out metallo-organic compounds, to understand their electrical signals and the interactions of these electron signals with genetic material. It would take a metallo-organic compound to restore the normal energetics to the abnormal cell.

I made thousands of compounds over the years, looking at the electrochemical reactions between these synthetics and DNA and RNA, all the while screening the compounds against the Ehrlich tumor, both in culture and in mice.

This was a period when I began to make porphyrins. If you're going to make porphyrins you'll need a dozen organic reagents, fifteen different metals to react with them, and functional side groups or chains to vary the porphyrin. You could work for years and make hundreds of porphyrins, and they might not be useful for anything. They might be compounds that were stable, though cures without a disease.

My general research method was to move through the metals and when one seemed more interesting than the others, focus on it. I've worked with all the transition metals at one time or another, going back and forth through the periodic table, returning to those that had promise, leaving behind those that killed too many mice.

The periodic table is the chemist's map. There are a few of them, but the one we use was developed by Mendeleev. You can use it at different levels of intensity or detail. The direct image of it hanging on the wall tells you about the great variety of natural elements. As you go up closer you see there are numbers all over it. And they tell you about the elements' reactivity and their atomic weights and numbers. An element's atomic weight is measured proportionately to hydrogen which has a weight of one.

The elements are arranged in vertical, horizontal and diagonal relationships which give descriptions of their reaction qualities. There are various groups such as the inert gases or the transitional metals. But this is all introductory. It's like when you go to a party and you're introduced to a group of people, but they're all different. And after a while you learn by talking to each of them that they are very different from one another even though they came together in a group. Maybe there's one that's particularly interesting. Maybe that person is attractive for some particular reason, so you begin to pay particular attention to learn about that person's unique qualities.

A lot of explanations are retrospective. Sometimes you just try a lot of things and you hope they'll work. I simply moved through the periodic table, believing that somewhere there was a catalytic event that would restore the energetics of the system.

I spent years with cobalt and thirteen years with vanadium, and studied reactions of molybdenum, tin, copper, and zinc. Even niobium and platinum. Eventually I got to palladium around 1990. These are known as the transition metals, and have d electron configurations which are extended out radially. Therefore they have an energy state which theoretically covers more distance and is more efficient for electron exchange.

The elements of the d electron group are the metals of industry. But instead of using them in a solid or in a mesh or as a metal surface I used them in liquid state. I made compounds out of biological molecules and d electron metals.

There are literally thousands of biological molecules and several dozen metals that are good candidates for catalysis at this level. As a result you have an enormous number of possible combinations, and you have to find your way through this maze. I cooked a lot of compounds, over twenty thousand in all. So I had to be at the microscope constantly, because for many years I did all the screening myself. I spent thirty years training on other metals before I got to palladium.

I can't say they were the wrong metals. They just didn't offer an effective therapy, though I learned what I needed to know working with them. In some part it was finally a matter of luck, but as much as luck it was persistence. There was an enormous amount of drudgery.

Chemists deal with everything around. If you're working for a paint company you work with different substances than if you're working in a biochemistry lab, or a paper mill or a mining company. So the things that you mix may come from the context, the business or the academic circle. If you're making beer, which is a fantastic way to begin the study of biochemistry, you're interested in fermentation and the conversion of grain to alcohol. And then you're interested in what could happen under other conditions and what to be wary of that could interfere with the process, and how much air, and how much sugar, and how much flavor to add, and when to filter it, and which type of beer is at the top of the vat, and so on. So beer making is chemistry.

Chemistry can be simple or chemistry can be complex. A chemical reaction can be as simple and common as putting a match to a piece of wood. You would be releasing the bonding energy in the wood to produce heat. Vibrational energy that was locked up in the connections between carbon atoms is now being transferred to oxygen to produce things like carbon dioxide. A source of energy which was locked up in a structure has now been converted to a new structure. In so doing there is extra energy left over which comes off as heat. So the mechanism of burning wood is that the cellulose molecules of wood interact with oxygen and give off things like carbon dioxide and perhaps carbon monoxide and other substances found in the wood, plus heat. In order to get the reaction going you have to heat it and that's called activation energy. We all know that it doesn't take too much energy to get the wood started, so the activation energy is paid back when the wood starts burning. It's very efficient in that way. You start with a little heat and you get a lot more later.

In chemistry we refer to *kinetics*. Kinetics likens chemical reactions to the functions of a machine. The things we're interested in is their efficiency, the proportions of substances that go in and go out, and the rates at which they are converted, just as when you're looking at a motor you're interested in how fast it turns and how much electricity it uses to turn to do a specified amount of work, and whether it overheats and doesn't run well. So the kinetics of chemical reactions are important, and they're looked at with instruments—with spectrometers for example.

You look at the product, what went in and what went out, and how much you needed to put in to get a certain amount out, and how long it took. Then you might plot the order of the reaction, which is a comment on how many substances are limiting for that reaction. In other words, if the rate of the reaction is dependent on the concentrations of one particular substance, that's a first order reaction, and if it's dependent on two substances that's a second order reaction. We're also interested in the reversibility of reactions. We also talk about long term kinetics. For example you might make a very nice substance, and over time it might precipitate, and become inert after a few hours. Does it stay clear in solution? Do its chemical signatures remain? Is it stable? Is it sensitive to heat or light? These are the things that allow us to understand the machinery of the molecular reaction.

When two or more molecular structures combine, they attach according to defined chemical principles. They donate or share electrons and form new

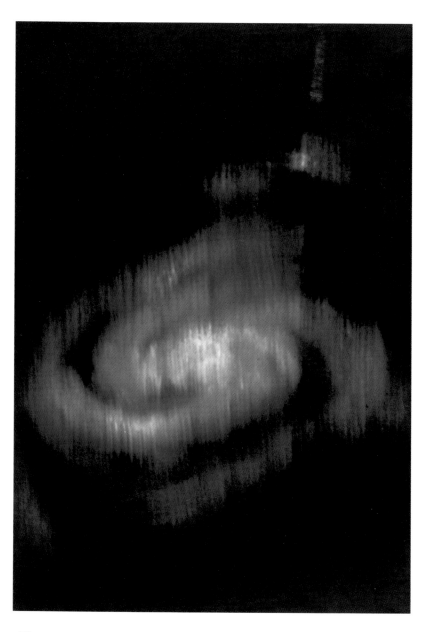

Chemistry can be simple or chemistry can be complex. A chemical reaction can be as simple and common as putting a match to a piece of wood.

structures. For example, a pair bond is two atoms sharing a pair of electrons. Benzene, for example, is the most common ring structure. It has six carbon atoms connected to each other in a circle, usually visualized as a hexagon. And there are six hydrogen atoms. These hydrogen atoms are attached to the carbon atoms, and the electrons from this compound are delocalized on a field leash. They exist in a pair of doughnuts above and below the ring. These two hazy clouds symbolized as doughnuts or *pi* clouds are part of its reactivity.

There's a lot of formalism in chemistry. We identify particular groups of compounds with characteristic spectra, characteristic solubility, and characteristic crystal structure. When they are isolated and purified into a crystal, you can actually refer to a diagram of the architecture of the molecule and how they're packed together to form that crystal. Because of this architecture, much like the architecture of a building, you have a mental image of the molecule. The geometry of the compound is how it's stuck together.

Early on I used Martel and Calvin's *Introduction to Metal Chelates*. I knew that metal catalysis as it existed in industry had to be consolidated for biology and medicine not into raw metal, but into metallo-organics. Making new compounds isn't so obscure. You can review compounds other people have made and decide, "I'll just make it a little different." Or "I'm going to make it again, but test it biologically." You don't always have to make it *de novo*. Any chemistry technician can put it together at the bench, from the literature. But you have to be aware that a great many things don't work, and they're nothing to be proud of. After you struggle for years and you get a few that work, you can define just those few with some measure of prediction. That doesn't, however, give you the scientific knowledge and technique to go out and invent another. You have to go through the same trial and error again if you want a different compound. You cannot expect something that's come through trial and error to deliver to you an easy route to another discovery. The basic rule is to get down in the hole and dig.

There's an awful lot of days when nothing works, when the mice die, when the chemicals fall out of solution, when the idea was bad and ill conceived. And you just can't imagine what you were thinking of when you went in and wasted that whole week.

Let's say you're making a new compound. In chemistry we have what is called the mole concept. A mole is a molecule's standard weight. If something has a weight of 50, 50 grams per liter is a molar solution of that molecule.

You cook a new reaction and then comes crystallizations, separations, filtrations, and purifications. And you end up with something that is crystalline or a homogenous precipitate or a nice liquid that has pure spectral character identity. Then you take it and isolate it and purify it by either using the liquid filtrate or the precipitate. Then you reconstitute this at physiologic pH and try and measure your concentration as best you can, then start checking it on biological systems, and cell cultures, and then in animals. This is not the beginning of therapy. This is the beginning of mouse killing. This is the very earliest stage. You are nowhere near healing.

Metals have been in nature forever. Organisms are extremely inventive, and their environments are woven within them. In turn the organism takes advantage of these substances which are needed only in tiny amounts. For example vitamin B12 contains cobalt. We need only microgram quantities of B12, but we definitely need it to live. Each metal has a different set of reactions. In my research, each metal was an art form. Each metal was full of tricks. Ruthenium, for example, has a very high specificity for a particular functional group not predicted in advance and not driven by increasing the energy of the locale.

Ruthenium is the most secretive, the most mysterious, the most discriminating and the most aggravating of all the metals. I was only successful in making some ruthenium compounds by the sheer number I made. I solved it by numbers rather than by intellect or chemical insight; by trying things that were somewhat related or that were interesting biologically. I can now make new compounds from ruthenium and we will do more of that in the future. But in the case of ruthenium, chemical principles didn't work in the sense that they didn't lead me to functional groups. The sheer massiveness of the screening process gave us the compounds.

With palladium we had the reverse. We had a wealth of compounds that all showed some (beneficent) properties. The trick was to make them safe with maximum potency. To make them safe, some metals like cobalt, must be sequestered inside a cage, as if you had a dangerous pet. You bring it inside your house in a cage. It can do tricks for you, but it has to remain in the cage. In the circus, the lion and the lion tamer are inside a cage so the worst that could happen is the lion tamer gets eaten, but not the audience. So I'm the lion tamer because I'm in the cage cooking chemicals. If I inhale cobalt or selinium and I die, the patients are safe. So you have to sequester the compound in a molecular cage. In these sandwich compounds, the organics are the cage.

Sandwich compounds are those where a metal is placed between two other compounds, usually large flat or planar organic groups, and the whole thing holds together. This is ancient in chemistry. So you make a little sandwich—two organics with a metal in between them. It could have been called an hors d'oeuvre or canapé, but we call them sandwiches. There are also double-deckers and triple-deckers, and polydecker compounds where you continue to stack metal on organic to rather great heights. You might call that a Dagwood complex. Some are open sandwiches where the metal sits on a single planar molecule.

Suppose I want to make copper acetyl-choline, which is a stable green compound. I'd use a tenth mole of copper and a tenth mole of acetyl-choline. Let's say my mind tells me that it should be two acetyl-cholines to one copper, and my solutions are all a 10th mole. I'd put out say five drops of copper and ten drops of acetyl-choline. So we made a "bis" compound. "Bis" means two. We now have bis acetyl-choline copper. You adjust the pH to physiologic, around 7.4. It's stable. It's a brilliant green. It looks good. It's interesting. You're using a fundamental substance in the organism. You're using a natural body metal. You make up a dilute solution of a hundredth molar. You withdraw the syringe. You put a tiny drop of it in the mouse. Before you've got the needle out of the mouse, it's dead.

Here is a great fundamental neural energy transmitter, one of the most important substances for electron transfer in the organism. So I'm thinking, I've just got to coordinate it, and its got to facilitate electron transfer. Maybe? Maybe NOT. At any rate the mouse dies before you get the needle out. It was a real compound, but a bad one.

This is just one of the energy transmitter groups that the body uses in very small concentrations to carry on the signaling within the central nervous system, and the peripheral nervous system. Therefore one would think they might be of interest. But they're lethal. You can't monkey with neural transmission. The organism won't tolerate it. It's delicately balanced. I learned not to touch the neural transmitters the hard way. The quickest way to kill an animal is to make a metal derivative of a neural transmitter, because you have suddenly knocked it out and put it on a different pathway.

A pathway in an organism is a major chemical event. For example, to make bones, there are cell surface enzymes called calcium ATP ases which are used to transfer calcium. It's one of the steps in an enormously complex process called a pathway. A pathway may be defined as a group of reactions. It may also be a cell cycle, which might be ten steps in which a larger substance, like sugar, is converted to a smaller substance like lactic acid. In order to cut it down from a six carbon to a three carbon it has to go through a variety of chemical and enzymatic steps. This is also referred to as a cycle. But they don't always rotate like the Krebs cycle. It's a system that the body uses that's well organized, that's tremendously important, and that must not be blocked for the organism to live and function. When I discuss the ancient pathways, I'm referring to the large series of steps.

Solutions are basic to chemistry. It's when things dissolve, as when you put sugar in your tea. Because the tea is warm it goes right into solution. It distributes well. It diffuses from the higher concentration to the lower concentration. So in a very short time most of your tea is sweet. The sugar molecules have become part of the water matrix of the tea. The solid sugar is

There are an awful lot of days when nothing works, when the mice die, when the chemicals fall out of solution, when the idea was bad and ill conceived.

gone. Nothing can be seen. The sugar is invisible but when you taste it you know it's there.

When you come upon an idea for a compound, you have to consider the geometries of each part. Sometimes they just don't fit. But you also have to consider their solubility. The metal may be fully soluble in alkali, usually, but in the presence of the organic group it's not sequestered within the water shell. You need to raise the pH and it then becomes very alkaline. Zinc is a good example. At a high pH Zinc forms a cloudy precipitate. If it's the metal, the chloride, or the salt and you raise the pH, it starts forming zinc oxides and hydroxides.

So if you complex it with an organic group and you raise the pH to 7-1/2 or 8, and you have a clear solution, you know the zinc is bound. It's hidden. You've got a new water shell. You know you made something, because zinc at pH eight looks like a white cloud and you now have a clear solution. You've connected it.

We talk about the size of molecules. A big molecule might be DNA or a protein. Enzymes are big molecules. They might weigh 300,000. A little molecule might weigh 200. I often worked with molecules that weigh from 200 to 500. In my experiments smaller molecules happened to work. This isn't wisdom, however, it's guerrilla warfare with the unknown. I simply had more success using small ligands than proteins or starches. Most of any investigator's time and effort are poured down the laboratory sink. But the negative data sculpts out the useful residue.

I selected the organic group because it had a biochemical pathway in the organism which is meaningful, which has something to do with energy transfer. And all we're doing with the metal is tuning it to the resonant frequency which increases the transfer of that same electron. Functional groups are things like amines, sulfides, hydroxyls, and carboxyls. These are small parts of biological molecules that stick out and react, and have the affinities for the metal, or they have a local effect that indirectly determines the solubility of the metal or the oxidation state of the metal. So I made a lot of compounds, but there were plenty that fell out of solution and went to the bottom of the bottle. The worst ones stayed around for a while, because they held promise. They were seductive. They seemed very endearing. They trapped me into hope and then dumped me.

I wish I could tell you I had an inspirational direction, but I just worked my way through the metals in the periodic table. For the organics I started with the metabolites, carbohydrates, nucleic acids, nucleotides, fatty acids, amino acids, vitamins, and derivatives of all those; a variety of analogs (things that are made to copy vitamins, nucleotides, or amino acids). Twenty thousand compounds later I had a point of view as to what I wanted to use. I don't think that before the 20,000 compounds I could have conceived in any way of the combination that was finally successful. Otherwise I wouldn't have made the 20,000 and spent 30 years. I could have done it in a year if I'd known where to go.

I believed that the energy transfer within the organism through the genes was terribly important. I believe that the difference between life and death is the transfer of energy through the genetic apparatus, and that we know a great deal about the genetic apparatus, but not how to make it alive. So the relation between the external energy and the gene energy became my focus. I wanted to know how the external energy got through and how it functioned. How it vibrated and how it produced product, and what its physical chemical parameters were a little bit lateral to what we knew about the metabolic schemes: the free energy states, and the configurations of molecules.

You've got to have faith in science, and that faith tells you it can always be done in another way. It's a long dreary road to travel by yourself, so you need other people who have faith in science to talk to. There are many days when you make a beautiful compound. It's green or a beautiful blue, then in 10 minutes it turns brown and falls to the bottom of the bottle. You shake it and you change the pH and nothing happens, it's still a brown cloud of gook. You can't measure it. It's obviously a mixture of something, and you can't get it back into solution. You try and adjust it with other functional groups, but nothing will change it.

When I first went to work in a psychiatric hospital, everything was very exciting. But in order to achieve a focus I had to construct an insulating barrier, like a cloud surrounding my head to exclude external madness so I could concentrate on my own internal madness. I learned not to see and hear what was around me when I was working. I developed it as an art in the hospital. All around me was madness but I learned to will it away.

One day a nice old lady came into my clinic, and I said, "How are we this morning." And she punched me in the nose. She said, "That's how we're doing this morning." She had come in for an examination, and I guess I came across as patronizing or saccharin. At any rate, she wasn't having it. It was a pretty good shot. It shocked me so much that I laughed. I said "Obviously you're not having any." She said "I'm not having any of you."

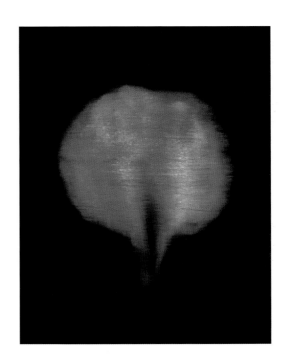

*Placing the prepared
dish on the micro-
scope's inverted
stage, I'd adjust the
lights and crank up
the lens, and sudden-
ly, there before my
eyes was this bril-
liantly glowing
world, completely
apart from the tur-
moil of the day. It
was like going to the
movies. Each time I
put in a different cul-
ture there was a new
show.*

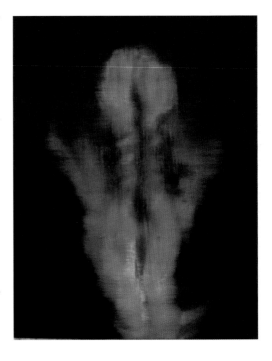

4. Under the Microscope

In the darkened clinic, with the chaos of treatment at an end for another day, I would prepare the cell cultures and ready the microscope to work late into the night. I had a practice of reworking my petri dishes, cutting out a small window in the base of each dish and gluing a piece of Saran Wrap over the hole. That way, when I raised the culture in the sterilized dish, I would have a thin window at the base to accommodate my lens.

Placing the prepared dish on the microscope's inverted stage, I'd adjust the lights and crank up the lens, and suddenly, there before my eyes was this brilliantly glowing world, completely apart from the turmoil of the day. If you have the dilution right, and the cells haven't piled up, you can look right into their internal structure. It was like going to the movies. Each time I put in a different culture there was a new show, and each time I added a catalyst or a reagent to the cell line it was a new act and scene; the brilliantly stained cells glowing with their own halos of orange and green. I could see the connections between cells and take satisfaction at having grown a new cell line. I'd watch them multiply or, when I was able to inhibit or poison the cancer cells, I'd watch them lose structure, break, and decline in the denouement of the final act, the death scene.

Carbohydrate metabolism refers to metabolic pathways in the cells within organisms that get energy from glucose. The first stage, the anaerobic stage, occurs in lower forms of life, such as amoeba and cancer cells, and also in higher forms such as mammals. The first stage converts glucose to lactic acid without the use of oxygen and is therefore called anaerobic metabolism. The aerobic is the second pathway. It appears in soil bacteria and certain protozoa, but is well developed in higher forms, such as mammals. In what we call differentiated tissue, the higher forms add two other cycles which are locked together for their efficiency. The first cycle takes pyruvate, which is in equilibrium with lactic acid, and converts it to carbon dioxide and water with ten enzymatic steps. This is the Krebs citric acid cycle. Locked tightly, integrated in the mitochondria, is the electron transport chain. Here electrons from various steps of the Krebs cycle pass through a series of enzyme reactions in particle structures. The electrons will go all the way to combine with oxygen to form water. And, at various stages, there are voltage jumps in this transfer. The energy is captured in reactions which preserve it as an organic phosphate called ATP. The two systems, the aerobic and anaerobic, work in sequence with each other in a normal cell. They both work with glucose. The aerobic just carries it further down, producing more energy.

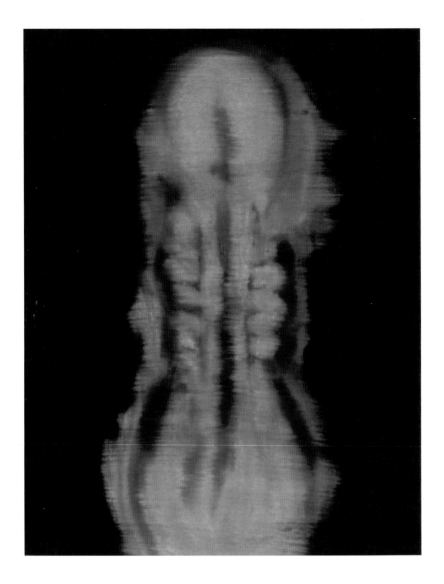

Modification and selection are the mechanism of evolution.
They're also the mechanisms of cellular evolution and cellular
processes. We can destroy most of the cells and allow a few to
emerge as those that are in natural equilibrium with the added
test substance. Our therapeutic mode is a selection that allows
the emergence of the aerobic clones within the cancer.

In both cases, the anaerobic and the aerobic, the ATP is made from the electron potential. The primitive anaerobic system can run a lot of glucose to lactic acid and produces a lot of energy. It just doesn't do it efficiently, because there's a lot of left-over material called lactic acid, which hasn't been used and is a potential fuel. So using this fuel and converting it the rest of the way is where we get the rest of the energy. This second stage is dependent on the use of oxygen. The large number of reactions that do that are much more efficient and produce 19 times more energy than the anaerobic system.

I was disappointed, as were others, that increasing the oxygen content in the cell cultures or in the organism's serum does not inhibit tumors. But it wasn't until many years later that I realized that oxygen transport in the cell had to compete with other gases within the cell such as carbon dioxide and methane and hydrogen sulfide; the main one being carbon dioxide. In June 1997 a group reported that the carbonic anhydrase enzyme is missing in a large series of colo-rectal tumors. This is an exciting report because carbonic anhydrase converts carbon dioxide to the liquid soluble carbonic acid. This would empty the gas ports and allow oxygen to flood in. So this deficiency in tumors would allow carbon dioxide gas to keep out the oxygen, and this sounds like a primary malignant deficiency and explains the Warburg defect in colo-rectal tumors.

The tradition has been that, faced with a metabolic difference between healthy and malignant cells, we must inhibit the cell's anaerobic state. My point, however, is not to poison the ancient anaerobic glycolysis but to restore the aerobic portion of the cell metabolism that's missing. By putting back the aerobic system one can restore the pathway. And in this way we can put a modifying stress on the primitive. The way the cells respond to that modifying stress determines the degree to which they will be selected out.

Modification and selection are the mechanism of evolution. They're also the mechanisms of cellular evolution and cellular processes. In a dish of cultured cells, we can modify and select. We can destroy most of the cells and allow a few to emerge as those that are in natural equilibrium with the added test substance. We usually have a reversion toward the malignant in cell cultures. Using a restorative system we should be able to convert toward the normal in the culture and in the organism. Our therapeutic mode is a selection that allows the emergence of the aerobic clones within the cancer.

Everything has its cycles and seasons, as has been historically and biblically noted. This is something that must be faced mechanistically as a fundamental event in nature. The human organism changes throughout its life, so that the baby doesn't grow up to be a large baby, but a new structure. It changes while an embryo in a more obvious way, but these kinds of changes continue to occur throughout the life of the individual. We might see the

65

later years as more obvious decay, but if we study the structure microscopically we will see that cellular death is present from the beginning. Cell death continues in order to create form by discarding portions of the whole so that a new form can emerge, much as the classical sculptor chips away pieces of the whole to expose the visible form within. In the organism, for example, to form the fingers as separate digits, the cells in between which form the webbing, must die. Then, in the living form, cells on the surface of the skin continue to be exfoliated and die to give rise to fresh layers of vigor. Blood cells have a limit to their life span of only 60 to 90 days before they are returned to the spleen. The gastro intestinal tract exfoliates dead cells from its lining. Bone reworks its form. The stomach, the mouth, and the other orifices shed their surfaces and bring forth fresh surfaces. The whole body remakes itself. The tissues regenerate, but some don't and are selected out in the growth of the form. Death gives rise to the living. The forces of life and death are intimate when we examine the form microscopically. And so too, chemically, there are selective forces which kill cells. In turn there are kinetics which are toxic at one level and selective of a surviving clone of cells at another level. So we relive in our form some of the history of the organism in its evolution. The ancient forms appear and are made anew.

I don't think this is morbid, but rather the realization that the external environment and the universe has always been an intimate force in the shaping of life. The outside, the exterior, the without, the unknown is incorporated with the inside, the within, the deep reactions of the organism. The without and the within communicate continuously. They form those metastable states which can survive the winnowing and selection forces around the organism.

We find the forms that survive to be beautiful. And the forms that survive, that we describe chemically and physically, are those with meta-stability. These forms, while transient, recur again and again. So too, beauty is fragile and fleeting, but emerges again and again. So too, all of life is fragile and passes quickly, but emerges again and again, because the resonant forms at the molecular level, the chemical level, the cellular level, all those things that have emerged in harmony against the selection of the without, are the stable states and the beautiful states. So beauty is eternal, but it is fragile. And this recognition of something going on within us should help us see who we are and where we come from, and where we can hope to go, because we are not separate from nature. Death is not separate from life, but merely another side of the coin.

In order for living organisms to function, the molecules and reactions that form them have to be around for a while. They have to be stable while they react with other molecules. They have to take part in building cell structures. Gene material must take energy and form proteins in complex events.

Proteins have a life time, and they need stability for a certain period. Those stabilities and harmonies are the organism. It is what we observe at a particular time as apparent stability of form, that we see with our eyes, even though this form is changing.

That stability in time units, when examined from the physical chemical view, can be described in wave theory, through instrumentation in the analytic laboratory. It sees characteristic energy peaks in gene material, for example. These resonant frequencies carry on reactions. They are not just the signature. They are the active vibrating life of that molecule. These energies and reactivities will interact with the other material that comes close to the genetic material. If we look carefully, we will see that reactions that transfer information and energy successfully have resonant wave interaction. They have a harmony of energy. They have a beat that's recognizable.

A great deal of my work has been to identify some simple things like the standing waves of genetic material. But before I got there, there were distinguished investigators who had already described the passage of electrical current in gene material. So the thrust of energy through structure is an every day event in biochemistry. Groundbreaking studies of electron transfer in DNA have been performed at Columbia, Cal Tech, and Georgia Tech. But the pulsing nature of DNA energy was first described by Bistolfi in 1990 in Genoa, Italy.

There is a harmony of the organism and a harmony in structure that allows the transfer of energy so that the organism can live and vibrate. So it can carry on its metabolism and its replication. Those harmonies and resonances must be perceived as inherently musical, because those harmonies recur and recreate the organism. It is not merely random information, but rather information which can function, and to survive to function means efficiency. Ultimately there is a musical or harmonic element within the organism which can recreate the patterns of information and energy. This is beautiful and resurgent. This is molecular music, fragile, dependent recurring under the right conditions, based in quantum echoes and hidden physics.

Now I theorize that electron transfer reactions favored the formation of DNA based genes over RNA based genes. DNA alone can absorb and buffer the cell against oxygen radicals. Oxygen radicals rapidly denature proteins at their sulphur sites. This protein denaturation is lethal. But the DNA acceptance of electron charge from oxyradicals, allows a variety of gene reactions favoring modification and selection of cells, ensuring survival.

It seems that organisms have learned to incorporate the environmental challenges into their systems and into their cycles. It's as if the environment becomes part of us. But the environment comes to us as stress. We can eat the environment as the environment eats us. But we are transfigured in the process. Electricity was first. It was the first meal. The first breakfast was electrons.

Throughout the years I was constantly thinking about metabolism and looking for the first yield of energy. For example, if you look at glucose metabolism, the first yield of energy is from a three carbon intermediate of glucose called phosphoglyceraldehyde. It gives off an electron to a co-enzyme that in its reduced state will be converted to an energy bond, an ATP bond. So in effect the electrons from phosphoglyceraldehyde were the first meal.

That first meal goes back to a very ancient cell. And the very first meal of all living things was a little spark. The higher forms have these sparks unpaired and in numbers. Oxygen is a very strong manufacturer and deliverer of unpaired electron sparks. So these oxyradicals were a stress on the cells.

Plants have these electrons because they learned to eat sunlight. The plants release oxygen while using sunlight to convert carbon dioxide and water to sugar. At the time of the first metabolic supper, some bacteria and protozoa began to modify and select. And they began to handle the unpaired electrons with rather large numbers of catalytic pathways with simple metal salts, and later on by proteins which the genetic apparatus creatively fashioned. So the protein charge transfer cycle emerged to handle radicals and make water out of them.

Now we have the electron/oxygen pathway to water. One of the more popular systems is the enzyme superoxide dismutase which converts superoxide (which is oxygen with one electron) to peroxide (which is a hydrated form of two unpaired electrons). There's also a whole bunch of peroxidases which split peroxide and make water out of it. And there's sophisticated enzymes called cytochrome p450 and cytochrome oxidase which also can handle this. So the number of ways and long words proliferate as you describe the adaptation to the presence of oxygen radicals.

Most molecules have a radical state if you just give them the right voltage and zap them. Vitamins form radicals. They're sold widely because they form a natural pathway to water. But it must be remembered that radicals are a part of nature, and are neither bad nor good in and of themselves. They are something that's internalized within us. Something we've learned to grow with, an essential part of nature. We live in a field of radicals. We exhale free radicals, and a halo of radicals floats over our heads and can be suppressed by a variety of drugs such as alcohol.

Billions of years ago, so the theory goes, oxygen, produced by the plants, came forth to increase the number of unpaired electrons. The ancient cells, of all shapes and sizes began to die in great numbers from the oxygen radicals in search of a partner. In other words, oxygen was once a pollutant.

If you have an unpaired electron or a radical it is very reactive and attacks molecules. Electrons tend to pair up in what we call an atomic orbital. They whirl about each other like twins. In cells, the radical state was too high an energy state to go unanswered. Living cells were injured by this instability, so they had to develop a new system to take care of radicals.

It's clear that organisms must eat or they will die. They spend a great deal of time eating and structuring their behavior around taking in energy. I believed from the beginning that energy had to go into the cell and that the inward flow of energy was somehow related to everything else in the cell. Look at sugar metabolism in the step where an electron is removed from a substance called phosphoglyceraldehyde. That electrical unit, that unit of potential, is accumulated in the organism in the cell and in multiple cells as a complex phosphate, ATP, but it originates as a bonded electron, a vibration.

And in all the assemblage of metabolism, and in all the cycles that we learn about in biochemistry, we see the scene repeated: the conversion of an electron transfer potential to a stored form of energy. In the variations of the organism, it always derives its energy from the electron. No matter what you are eating: carbohydrates, proteins, or fats (storing them as one molecule or another, as ATP or acyl bonds or fats)—you always start with that electron, and you accumulate that electrical potential, and your body conducts chemical events based on that electrical potential. That electrical potential is what we should measure and attend to in the flow of ions, salt and water, and in the fall out assemblages of ATP.

Cells, as we know them, have a very defined chemistry, and when we lay it all out in flow sheets we do it as if it's rigid and defined. But in nature we know that life is not static. For example, even if you grow cells in culture they change a lot over time. Strange things happen to them that aren't predictable. They mutate quickly, often toward the primitive. The external is a problem, even in cell cultures. So if we let in nature, which includes time, we have the inexorable. This is an inevitable step, bringing an infinite number of unknowns which will select out large numbers of cells. Dryness, heat, starvation, toxins, parasites, waves, and rays—challenges of all kinds. The external intrudes into the gases and the fluids of our bodies. The variations in the small molecules, and the subtleties of things we are not aware of in the living broth, will select, and out of this selection will come a new form. And in two or three days the culture is looking strangely different, even though it's a clearly vigorous thing like a baker's yeast. And if you grow it in an unusual broth, and expedite an appetite and a quality, pretty soon you have a new strain.

The external intrudes continuously. It intrudes in plasma. It intrudes in blood. It not only intrudes on the outside of the cell, but comes into us at the most intimate levels of information transfer. It twists and turns and makes things grow differently. We are not insulated. We are not isolated. We are an open window to nature. The external is all through us. It structures us.

Problems arise because of our denial of this fact. We typically see the organism as a defined entity. But we are fashioned of the universe, and the universe streams through us.

The universe, the external, is an onslaught and an interaction which modifies and selects at the cellular and molecular level continuously. It should come as no surprise, because it is part of the organism's journey. But if we choose to understand these events that make us one with the universe, we must understand this journey, so that we can avoid certain changes that cause disease, and untimely death. We must understand the organism's journey so that we can restore vigor and persist.

Therefore I searched for the chemical reactions in the early stages of the embryo in order to restore them in the mature organism in the presence of disease. The journey involves an overwhelming number of enzyme sets and gene sequences, but I saw them as labile and susceptible to the external, and therefore vulnerable. Fortunately we've been able to mimic these enzymes. I have devised metallo-organic catalysts, so that we have substitutes, which can be made in a uniform, stable way suitable for pharmaceutical approaches. These mimic the protein without actually being protein.

Now the cell must have a communication system by which it apprises the entire organism of the food available, in order to function. This energy inventory must always be present, and the communication must always be quick. But if we realize it's electrical, we know that this is the easiest and fastest kind of energy both for storage and communication. There are a lot of ways to wire a cell for communication, and there are lots of ways to make capacitors for the cell, for storage of energy.

During those years while I worked my way through thousands of compounds, I maintained a firm prejudice: that billions of years ago higher forms evolved out of the lower forms, and I simply had to find a way to reproduce it. I posited that it happened, in every embryo, in every conception and birth in the higher forms. The dividing fertile egg's cells stick together. And though each is a separate singular undifferentiated cell it doesn't wander off alone, but clusters with other cells in a ball called the morula. Shortly after that, the cells of the morula hollow out to form the blastula. Then, like a deflating basketball, the blastula collapses in on itself to form a double walled vessel called the gastrula. And then where the lips of the folded form meet, new cells arise which are different in form than any before, and these are the first specialized cells called the primary mesenchyme. These cells grow between the other two layers and have in them tiny fibers called collagen. These cells become the connecting tissue between cells. These are the first specialized cells.

In these aerobic cell systems there are a number of changes. The first metabolic mechanism is designed to admit the oxygen. This is carbonic anhydrase. The next one is the charge transfer species, which takes the charge from the oxygen radical and conducts it through the radius of the cell to the center, to the DNA, and creates an electrical field. These mechanisms form the inward current. After these two mechanisms, a third arises, which takes the electrons at a receptor site and puts them on an oxygen molecule to make peroxide, then hydrates it to make hydrogen peroxide. It then splits the peroxide to make hydroxyl radicals, and donates these to the surprisingly ancient enzyme product, pro-collagen. Then the pro-collagen flows out, not as a gelatinous liquid, but as fiber, to become mature collagen, which binds cells into tissues. This is the outward current. The schematic is complete. The cell has its first pulse, which makes an active energy exchange between the internal and the external, at a higher level than had been found before in nature. And this first pulse resonates with many other cells, and the packed cells carry on their pulsations with the environment. They resonate with each other and set each other off by inductive influence so that their pulses increase. And the tissue pulses appear, and the heart beats and the brain discharges and the muscles evolve. The organelles modulate and use this in contractile structures, converting the pulse to organic phosphates and other high energy bonds. But the cell pulse is first and provides the raw electrical energy for all the physiologic pulses.

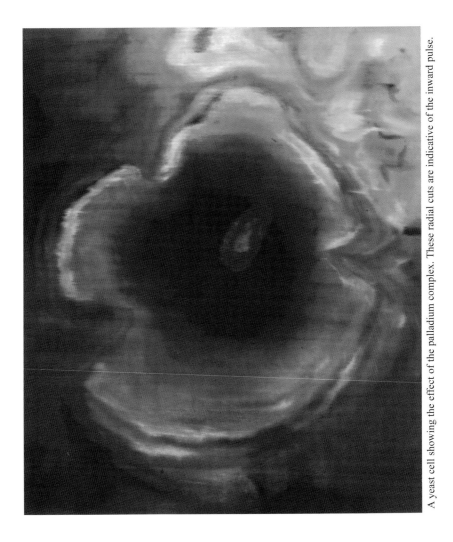

A yeast cell showing the effect of the palladium complex. These radial cuts are indicative of the inward pulse.

In the early 1990's, after producing and screening over 20,000 compounds. After trying most of the transition metals, continuing down and to the right along the periodic table, I turned to palladium and found what I had been searching for.

5. The Mice Stopped Dying

Originally there were 8000 patients at Central Islip State Hospital. When I left there were about 400 or 500. They had been releasing them over the years. The people I had cared for found their way onto the streets and had to fend for themselves. As the State hospitals began to close there was a great loss of the spirit of the place. It's not just that there was less work. There was less vitality, less structure, and less efficiency. It was as though a sickness hung over the place. As it drew to a close, I began to want to get out. By the time I left, it was closing down. It no longer had a research division. Two years before I left that budget item was cut.

I left Central Islip State in 1986 and moved my electrochemistry equipment to the Hematology Laboratory at the Northport V.A. Hospital. It was a welcome opportunity to work with an oncologist, but, unfortunately, it was a lab full of switches from incubators, freezers, and centrifuges. It was hard to get clean readings. There would often be a spike on them which would drive me up the wall.

After working at the Northport V.A., I needed a quiet space, free of the glitches caused by other electrical equipment. I had always done some work in my basement lab at home. Over the years I'd had mice there, and used it as a second or third workspace. Now it became my primary lab and I brought my electrochemistry equipment there, where I could work any time night or day.

There was never a lull in my research. I had hunches all day long. They had to be supported or eliminated—working through the choice of metal, the pathway, the first and second ligand. I had a hunch about how to measure it chemically and a hunch about how to measure it biologically.

My family was always there doing things to help me. It became automatic. There was technical assistance; pouring, mixing, and cooking. There were mice to be injected and many tasks that weren't dramatic, but were very supportive because we did them together in the knowledge that they would lead to something. We did science in a great field of activity without it being the dominant subject in our lives, because we lived ordinary lives. There was the beach and boats and tennis and parties and the garden and all sorts of family events. From the earliest days I'd take the kids to the lab to look into the microscope.

Everyone in my family had their own dedication to a career, each in a different field. But it wasn't the only thing in our lives. My wife Hoda is a dedicated photographer, who worked professionally for many years. My son Wade is trained in physics, electronics, and music, and works with me in the lab. My daughter Joy is an artist who began as a biologist only to leave science for art, which curiously enough led her to painting interpretations of technical visions.

We all supported each other in our separate interests. No one's obsession was greater than another's. We were all dedicated, and it seemed natural. I also raised mice in the basement of my house, and when they died as they often did until the discoveries of the early 90s, I buried them in my garden by the rose bushes. I did this myself, keeping it from my children. It wasn't easy in the middle of the night in the middle of winter when the ground was frozen. I'd have to dig to a decent depth. The trend of pet burials did catch on, however, so we had a goldfish cemetery and one for snails and other creatures from the fish tank. We also buried inch worms which the kids collected. Every creature was entitled to a decent burial. We had a pet cemetery.

I was never happy about losing a mouse. If they were pets of anyone, they were pets of mine. Theoretically, it's the failure of an experiment and the loss of a creature. Unless it was turned into meaning, it was just a mess. It had its appropriately somber moments and meanings. But I did it for people, not for the glory of the abstraction, or the adventure of science.

The nice thing about having an electrochemistry apparatus in my basement was that if I had a bright idea at 2 AM I didn't have to wait until the morning light to test it out. I could just run down stairs and do the experiment. And, as a bonus, most of the electrical switches and lights were off, so I got a cleaner reading when everyone else was asleep. I'd run down in my pajamas and bed slippers and go to work.

I would usually challenge DNA to change its free energy with a substance that came to mind in my early morning wakefulness. I would make up a combination, measure it, set the controls and run it on the polarograph. It was basically a matter of what I was going to put in the specimen cup and what else I would add on top of it. I'd take a metal bonded to an organic, see what compound they would form, and what charge they would carry, and if it was reversible. I'd have a vague geometric form in my head. I'd go down make it, and put it in the machine, run a signal, and go back to bed. It was no fuss no muss, like going down for a glass of milk.

After I made a compound I'd run a ramp of current through a sample cup with the compound in it. I'd usually bubble nitrogen through it for eight minutes—it's called purging—to get rid of the oxygen curve so I could read the signal of the compound. And then I'd have a signature. I'd look for a wave from zero to minus a volt, and see if there was some juice—a nice sine wave. I'd see if it held current. As I'd raise the ramp of voltage—if it has a charge density in that range—it would be influenced by the scan. I'd scan it forward and in reverse, which would show if it gave charge up faster than it took it. It's called voltammetry. A lot of molecules will take up charge, then give it off. If you cross the rug and lint sticks to your clothes and then you touch

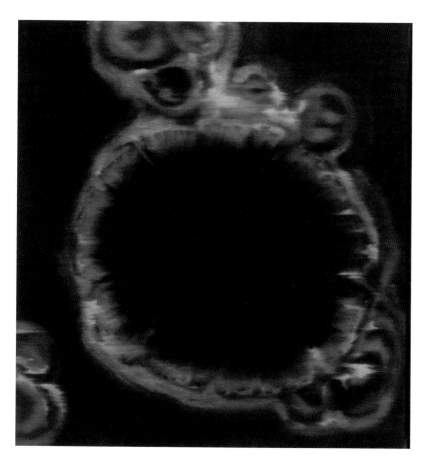

The nice thing about having an electrochemistry apparatus in my basement was that if I had a bright idea at 2 AM I didn't have to wait until the morning light to test it out. I could just run down stairs and do the experiment.

something you may get a spark. So you picked up a charge and you gave it off. Now the relative size of these signals told me the trend of that compound, whether it's likely to have an equilibrium, mostly to hold or mostly to donate. Then, after I got that signal, I would add the biological challenge. I'd watch the signal—the top signal, the reducing signal—drop and move to the left as the juice was given off to whatever I'd added. It was a very clear event. The next question was, if a lot of juice left, did it leave slowly or quickly?

It's a little like the stock market. When you invest in a stock, and you're lucky, you watch the price of the stock rise. And, after a while, you start drawing the money out. And you read and plot the interest. How much you've stored up and how much you can take back. Obviously the more you put in the more you can take back. Sometimes it depends on the rules of the bank (market) and there are penalties for withdrawal. A molecule does this too but with current instead of cash.

Molecules will hold or store current at particular voltages. Or there may be a smooth rise in the current being held until it reaches a certain voltage point and then the current will descend. These are what we refer to as the voltage peaks. This has to do with the atomic configuration and the electrons that are added in particular ranges and the characteristics of that molecule.

What you see on the computer screen is a graph with a line forming what looks like a hill going up to the right, which is the convention, and then an upside down hill coming back to the left on the screen. Above the line, the hill rising up and to the left, is the current being put in, and the upside down hill, reaching down under the line, is the current being given back.

Let's say you scan from zero to minus one volt. Voltage has a convention that's different than current. The signs are reversed. So increasing the number of electrons in voltage is what we call reducing. It has more negative potential. So you scan toward more negative potential, toward more reducing force in which the instrument loads the molecule with electrical current. And after the instrument gets to minus a volt and you start decreasing the voltage, so you're now oxidizing, or pulling the electrons back. The characteristic voltage ranges are passed through. They become molecule-characteristic because the current or the height of that hill or the slope of that hill varies and ends up with changes in direction we call peaks. You also have a reverse, or anodic peak, an upside down hill. These wave forms are the molecule's electronic signature.

If you take the average point between those two peaks, which is called a standard potential, it represents the behavior of that atom under those parameters: the scan speed, the drop size of the electrode, the particular electrolyte at a particular pH. You set up a standard system so you can look at a molecule in a particular way, electronically, which is representative of its electrical behavior; its reduction and oxidation in that particular voltage range. So now you can add another substance to it, one that doesn't read in that range. Let's say we add DNA, which doesn't read in the minus voltage range, so that any electrical influence on that substance will be read purely by the change in the molecular signature.

If the additional substance changes the electrical character in a range in which that substance doesn't read, you set about deciding how the new substance did that. In what direction it changed its electrical character. Did it add electrons to it or did it take them away. If the reduction hill shrinks, you've lost electrical charge. The area under the reducing curve encloses a space, an integral, which describes the capacitance of the molecule. As that capacitance drops, that charge is lost to the material you've added. So now you see that the charge has gone from the drug being studied to the DNA. That means that the drug has been oxidized or has lost charge, and the DNA has been reduced or has gained charge.

The rate at which the hill disappears is of great importance. For example if we run a scan over and over, the number of scans it takes for the reducing hill to disappear is the interval necessary to get rid of the charge. So if it happens right away you have a rapid effective reaction.

I had carried out these procedures thousands of times, looking for a compound that would transfer charge safely and effectively. Then, in the early 1990's, after producing and screening over 20,000 compounds, after trying most of the transition metals, continuing down and to the right along the periodic table, I turned to palladium and found what I had been searching for.

I had made three such palladium compounds at once, and they all appeared to be on the right track. I knew that these had nice solubility and color, therefore I had a compound and it was in solution. The question was did it do anything?

When I tested them electrochemically, they did the electron transfer rapidly and it was easy to measure. So the more rapidly and efficiently one could transfer electron charge to DNA, the more effective was the potency against cancer in the screen. The major event occurred on the electrochemistry instrument. I got a beautiful tracing, because when I challenged DNA in 15 cyclic passes most of the signal disappeared and transferred to the DNA. That was the most important signal I ever observed. Everything else was to refine it, to make it do a single pass conversion. I knew then which way I was going. I knew what the reaction was.

That first compound did nicely, but took 15 scans to get rid of all the juice. So I made some derivatives and pretty soon it got rid of the juice in five scans. And I kept going and pretty soon it got rid of the juice in two scans. I kept making derivative compounds until it got rid of the juice in one scan. And I thought, Wow, that's a fast reaction. The thing loads up with nice

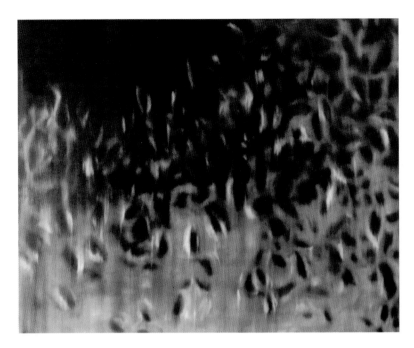

Monkey kidney carcinoma untreated (top) and treated (bottom) with the palladium complex.

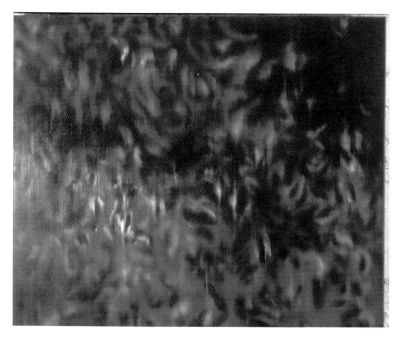

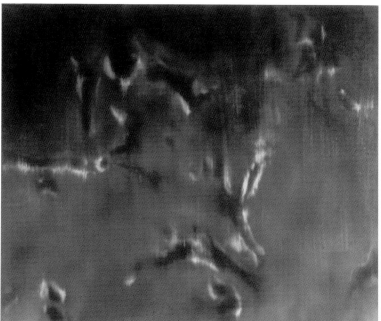

Monkey kidney carcinoma untreated (top) and treated (bottom) with the palladium complex.

big sine waves and then it gives it all off, bang, to DNA.

Next, I placed it in the Ehrlich carcinoma cell culture. I looked at it under the scope and saw all the tumor cells getting shredded. The tumor cells are like big round balls. I watched the dense chromatin form in the cancerous cells, the nucleus forming a "C" shape like a copyright symbol. Initially I saw three dots, then they pulled together. This was dense chromatin. I had blown up a lot of Ehrlich cells, but for the first time I had a warning. It had been nearly 30 years since I had the first successes in causing dense chromatin, by adding respiratory substrates to the Ehrlich carcinoma.

While all this was happening, the other part, outside the nucleus, called the cytoplasm, was losing its halo and turning gray. Then I saw obvious leakage of cell content out to the exterior. After that, the cells began to leak and collapse rather uniformly. I saw the cuts and breaks forming in the cell membrane begin to ooze. Then there was just a lot of garbage and it was all sticking together.

The rate of destruction was cell cycle related. In other words all the cancer cells were suffering, but in slightly different states and forms, because some of them were in division and some were between division. Of course I had seen cell destruction many times before with toxic materials. So the next question was, is this a toxic substance? I injected it into a healthy mouse. I gave it a big jolt in the morning, then another one at night. The next morning I rushed downstairs to see if it had buried itself in the sawdust and died, but it was still there, running around. The next question was, will it do anything to a tumor in a mouse?

The Ehrlich carcinoma is a really mean tumor. You dilute a serum form of it 10 to 1 in saline, and inject a tenth of a cc into the abdominal space of a mouse and in four or five days it starts to swell. In 12 days it's dead. If you're going to do an animal study, you do six test subjects who get the treatment and six controls. You get 12 mice and inject the Ehrlich tumor and get started.

There are various habits about how you treat. The usual habit is that you give the tumor a day head start. With the palladium compound we gave it four or five days head start. I thought maybe the first experiment would only be inhibitory. I thought we might get a sense of how long the mice would survive with the new drug. Instead we knocked out the ascites (the swelling caused by the tumor). I couldn't believe it. In 12 days all the controls were dead and my other mice, even though I didn't start treatment until the fourth or fifth day, were running around. And they hadn't increased in their belly size. I kept them on treatment and worried about things like artifact: (I put a needle in, maybe the tumor leaked out.) To test further, I injected into the skin of the back and the tumors still went down. So 30 days later I've still got the six mice and I'm doing cage cleaning and feeding. The results were undeniable. This was a real drug.

Six months later, I repeated the experiment and had about two dozen mice that were still alive. There was some recurrence in the inguinal region. Most of the tumors disappeared. Some did not, but set up in the lymph nodes and about two months later I found solid tumors in the inguinal region. That was also treatable; I was able to make those break down as well. I had these mice around for a year and a half, and I was tired of cleaning cages. So I had to let them go. I have a rule in the lab. If you cure a mouse you have to let it go. You can't give it the tumor again. I had to find secret haunts for them. I don't believe in double jeopardy. I hope those first mice to be cured of the Ehrlich carcinoma lived a long life.

Then we developed a program. We treated dogs and cats. I started palladium research in 1990. In 1993 I filed for a patent. Two years later, October 31, 1995, it issued. Then, two more patents were granted.

We were looking at a new kind of drug, a new kind of medicine, and the question was, what was the mechanism by which this substance interacts to treat disease? I'd been doing electron transfer chemistry on these groups for a long time. So now, much to my delight, I had shown that palladium lipoic acid transferred charge to DNA, and that you could make a compound that was therapeutic, using this principle.

I located the origin of the charge being transferred within the membrane fats of the cell. It appeared the new drug was a shunt, a carrier of electrical charge, which had both a source and a place to target. This is an ideal kind of kinetics. The compound would be regenerated within the cell to do its job. It would not bind. It would only transfer. So if the pathway for electron transfer from fats to DNA was a natural pathway, related to development, then it would not be toxic. And if it had a therapeutic effect against the primitive, against the tumor, then we would find that it would be a modification and selection force. It would select out the tumor. The mechanism by which this occurred was the subject of my research. The exciting thing was that it appeared to be true that a natural pathway of electron transfer was both a modifier and a selector for an aerobic cell line requiring electron transfer. A whole new world had come to us after years of struggle. Suddenly there was safe therapy. There were questions to be looked at, but surely there would be answers.

Next we broke through into the cofactors that are related to that kind of reaction of nucleotide reduction. There is a whole biochemistry literature on nucleotide reductases which is in the texts. It wasn't terribly difficult once we broke through to do variations on a theme, and enrichment of the pathway. Because those things that work did have electronic interactions which fit our instrumentation.

We're now rushing down this road of efficient electron transfer into the cell. We've found that there is also an outward transfer in which the electron is now a different radical, a hydroxyl radical and that the hydroxyl radical leaves the cell in several pathways. One, we think, is collagen. It forms a fundamental matrix which binds cells into tissues. The other, we think, goes to parts of myelin to form normal myelin in the brain and nervous systems. This raises promise for certain difficult diseases of the neurologic system. So if we have an inward current and if we have an outward current, we have a model for a cellular pulse.

Throughout the search for therapeutic compounds, my prejudice that we could restore the aerobic system through modification and selection, allowing the emergence of the aerobic clones within the cancer, has remained steadfast. This is the thrust of the electron transfer work with the palladium complex. It will be the same thrust of theory as we restore carbonic anhydrase to other tumors, and prolyl hydroxylase in the mesodermal tumors, the sarcomas. We should find drugs which are non-toxic because these enzyme pathways already exist in the normal cells and in the host organism.

The more you look at it, the more the fundamentals grow. Palladium has pure d electron configurations. It's the metal's metal. It has the most d orbital configurations of any atom in the universe. So if I had but known, I would have gone there first. But I wouldn't have been ready. I did not preconceive palladium as an answer to metal coordination medicine. It was done empirically. When I got to palladium I was ready for another metal. Somewhere there was energy transfer at the gene level that was meaningful and useful.

Throughout the years, I have looked for the developmental enzymes. These are mystery enzymes. Everybody wants to know why the cell develops into something different. As you grow older, you become a different creature. We can only study the individual reactions which are definable and clear, but in the cell we have a concert being played. It has a prelude in the baby and the small child, then an overture in the adolescent, then the recurring themes of the mature adult and finally the old—all because of the mystery developmental enzymes. Now I'm not saying that the enzymes are producing anything different as time passes, but that enzymes turn on and off. A new enzyme comes on the stage. There are new players as the drama unfolds. It's gene expression, and what we bring here to genetics is the suggestion that the developmental reactions rely heavily on energy. I refer to this as electrogenetics. Electrogenetics is a new subject. We point to it. We point to possibly three enzymes that I have devised and copied in catalytic ways which seem to cause development, and which can be used to treat tumors, but that's just the tip of the iceberg.

There are three types of enzymes and gene site reactions which allow the electrical polarization of the cell. These groups are called: 1.The oxygen vehicle system, which is the indirect effect of carbonic anhydrase; 2. The

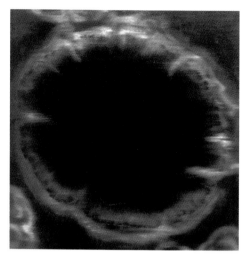

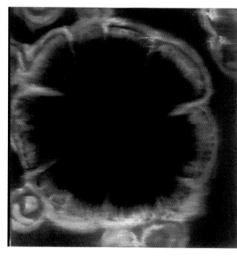

I thought maybe the first experiment would only be inhibitory. Instead we knocked out the ascites (the swelling caused by the tumor). I couldn't believe it. In 12 days all the controls were dead and my other mice were running around.

electron transfer system which we call nucleotide reductases; and 3. Prolyl hydroxylase which allows the outward current. I have synthesized all three artificially and they represent for us a theory. We hope to develop others so we can restore all the deficits in electrical polarization and maturation.

The nucleotide is a single step in gene material and the nucleotide reductase exists to actually make DNA. So artificial DNA reductase is another step after the DNA is made and continues to reduce or add electrons to it. It's another level. And I suggest if I can make it that it's already there. I postulate that there is a DNA reductase existing naturally.

The other two enzymes that I've synthesized are clearly there. One is prolyl hydroxylase which forms mature collagen which is the fibrous protein matrix which binds cells together and which is the dominant protein made in all mammals. The other enzyme, carbonic anhydrase, converts carbon dioxide to a hydrated or bound water form, carbonic acid. I feel that this is a crucial early developmental enzyme.

I think that carbonic anhydrase may be the first devel-

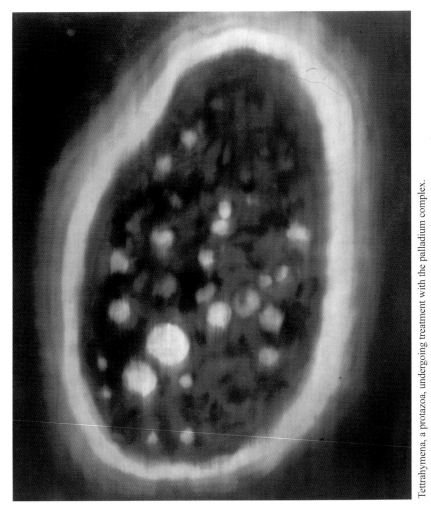

Tettrahymena, a protazoa, undergoing treatment with the palladium complex.

It appeared the new drug was a shunt, a carrier of electrical charge, which had both a source and a place to target.

opmental enzyme. What it does by lowering the gaseous carbon dioxide in the cell, is allow the entrance of oxygen along the surfaces where gases do not mix easily. This surface instead is one binding gas with a high stability constant. So if you get rid of the carbon dioxide, then the air comes in and the oxygen has the next highest affinity for the cell surface. So that's how oxygen begins to come into the cell. Oxygen of course is a great electron

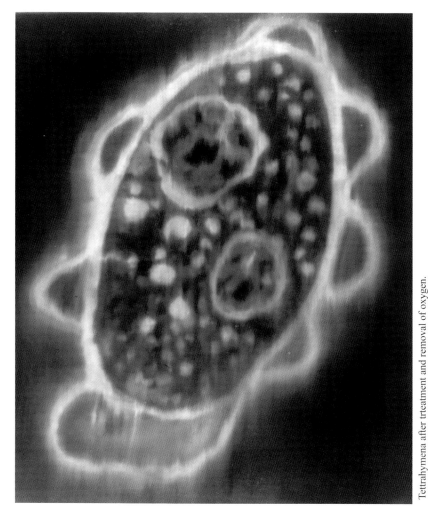

Tettrahymena after trteatment and removal of oxygen.

The cytoplasm, was losing its halo and turning gray. Then I saw obvious leakage of cell content out into the exterior. After that the cells began to leak and collapse rather uniformly.

carrier. So one begins to talk about electron transfer and oxygen radicals shortly after we allow oxygen to come into the cell.

The next stage, DNA reductase, is an electron transport reaction which is naturally influenced by the presence of oxygen. The availability of electrons to it is greater in the presence of oxygen.

The third enzyme, prolyl hydroxylase, forms collagen by putting a hydroxyl radical on pro collagen. This is also a product of electron transfer.(with several steps removed from the initial). Prolyl hydroxylase is well described in the chemistry texts. When I made this enzyme, it made collagen. I realized that the gene was already present and I was just doing the last step, because I induced it right away. So that the transfer of oxygen radical species to procollagen was a simple experimental model which bore out very well in the electrochemistry.

So now we had two parts of the inward current; the admission of oxygen and the transfer of electrons. And we had one part of the outward current; the transfer of hydroxyl. What we had was three reactions that describe development; admission of oxygen, the transfer of electrons, and the outward transfer of hydroxyls. They are all very compatible and interrelated. You can't make a hydroxyl without oxygen or without electrons or their water products. So far these three are the lead developmental enzymes of electrogenetics.

I made 30 palladium compounds. About the 15th compound, I had pretty much narrowed it down. I was going to make palladium lipoic acid. I didn't know I was going to trimerize it. I didn't know I was going to make the other factors for it and solve the problems that were attendant with it. But I had the palladium lipoic complex. We did a lot of things with yeast. Yeast is harder to kill than tumor cells. One of the things we had as an early problem was that the drug caused fevers, because it's a charge transfer and has a thermal equivalent. So I created a buffer for it. And it was really done rather quickly. I'm proud of it. My son Wade was with me when we worked it out. It seems that the palladium complex causes a 3-1/2 degree centigrade rise in the yeast culture at the therapeutic dose. So I made the buffer and that caused a one degree rise when studied alone. We had a very fine thermocouple. It read in hundredths of a degree. And we had a recorder. And we had a beaker of yeast culture wrapped in layers and layers of paper towels to insulate it and we had it on a rocker platform we bought just for this and we'd shoot drugs into a port and record over a couple of hours. Next we combined the buffer with the palladium lipoic complex. We injected the mixture into the culture and measured temperature for two hours. There was no temperature rise at all. Wade and I realized the mechanism at the same time. We said, "Opposite charges," in unison. We realized that if you transfer electrons and protons at the same time you are moving a neutral hydrogen atom, and there is no heat. I had eliminated the fever response.

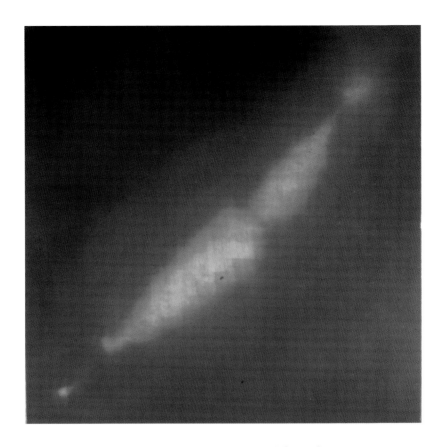

Most people know that structure is not life. Life is responsive-ness and vitality. It's all the delight in movement and behavior and feeling. It's the energy flow in the structure. Being alive is when your dog jumps up on your couch and barks.

6. Energy is the Shake in Things

Most people know that structure is not life. Life is responsiveness and vitality. It's all the delight in movement and behavior and feeling. It's the energy flow in the structure. The degree to which structure supports energy flow is the degree to which we have a viable organism. So then we start to look at structure a little differently, asking what is it doing that makes it alive? Being alive is when your dog jumps up on your couch and barks.

When you study physiology and cell physiology you learn a great deal about the movement of salts and ions and calcium and magnesium and sodium and potassium and chloride and bicarbonate and so on. But even that which begins to describe the flow within the structure seems to lack that integrating force that explains what it is to be alive. What is the major living event in this bag of proteins, gene material and stuff that makes it responsive? Because of this question I searched for the flow of energy at the gene level.

Anyone who owns a lap top knows that if the battery goes dead and you don't have a power cable handy you don't have a computer, no matter how many megs of RAM it has. Everyone talks about information transfer in the computer, but little is ever said about the power source.

With this in mind I often ask what the difference is in the genome of a living and a dead creature? You see the genome is the same, but the energy flow in the dead structure is missing. The diagrammatic structure of the cell is problematic because the diagramatic cell is dead. When we study metabolism in biochemistry we see a lot of diagrams of the conversions of sugar, fats, proteins, and gene material but it still doesn't look alive. It's still a bunch of diagrams. The cell's physical chemistry adds some numbers to the diagrams, but it still doesn't look very alive. What is needed is an idea about what it is that's alive.

Energy is the shake in things. It is rapidly converted from molecular shake, and electron shake to a very localized hum in a bond between two chemicals, then to heat or the emission of light from the shaking of electrons by the voltage. Everything is convertible, and they're all forms of energy. The cell, the tissue, the organ, the house, and the utility company agree that electrons are the best way to manage energy and convert it to all uses, from biological systems to appliances which make light, mechanical, sound, or heat energy. In New York State electrical energy comes in part from the Niagara River, and is transformed into many things from household lights to the heat that boils the water in the coffee maker, but it's never destroyed. It may however be dispersed. It's particularly difficult to capture heat because it runs in all directions; through your fingers so to speak, and it's gone unless

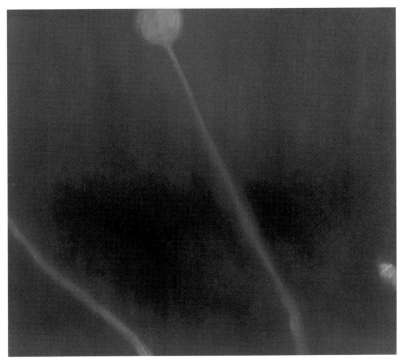

When we deal with a biological system, it isn't surprising that the ancient form of energy released is that of an electron jump from one molecule to another.

you have an insulated container, like a steam engine to drive a piston.

When we deal with a biological system, it isn't surprising that the ancient form of energy released is that of an electron jump from one molecule to another. As organisms evolve they become more complex. The number of protein enzymes which handle electrons increase greatly and electron energy is stored in chemical bonds called ATP. The highly efficient system can make more ATP.

A few gene sites govern a massive increase of energy within the cell and determine by this process, the special geometric changes within the earliest embryo stages. These reaction mechanisms must be repeated in each newly formed cell, after every cell division, if the cell is to develop normally. These major state-determining reactions occur in three forms and their presence is both modifying and selecting. It can heal and it can destroy. Each plays a crucial part in normalizing cell development. The three are closely interactive. Together they provide the energy which changes the forms of biologi-

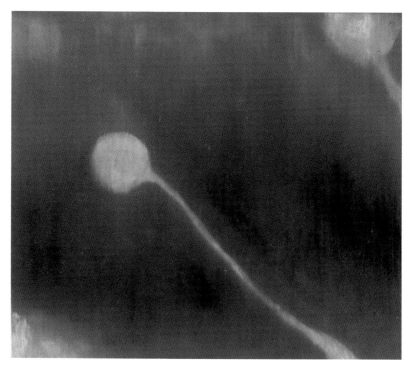

It's a bounce, it's a spark. Your spark plug is not bound to your piston. It just sparks it. Similarly, electro-active drugs are not bound to their receptors.

cal molecules by a force called polarization. They admit oxygen to the cell, conduct charge through the cell, and form a matrix between the cells. The three reactions account for the physical contortions of the early form of the fertilized egg. They are then maintained through the life of normal aerobic cells

As we know, the molecules in the Krebs cycle are dismembered of their charge by proteins, and then the electrons are transferred. The energy runs down hill. And down at the end of the hill is oxygen with a tremendous hunger for electrons. But it wasn't until years later that I realized there was also DNA with an even greater hunger for electrons.

Marcus described electron transfer as driven by the force of voltage, and impeded by the energy needed to constantly reorganize the molecules involved. There are numerous papers on charge transfer, but I don't think you can really understand charge transfer until you look at alternating current theory. The propagation of electrons, electron transfer, is, at first, very sophisticated when described by looking at the molecule that's holding it, or by looking at the matrix, or by looking at the solvent. These are terribly important, and Marcus's theory is fundamental in this description. But you have to remember that Marcus's transfer is Direct Current, and until you get into AC you don't really get high efficiency electron transfer.

If I hadn't gotten into electrochemistry and into frequency analysis I wouldn't have begun to appreciate the marvelous events of AC and pulse currents to get juice to where it's supposed to go. Because in an alternating current, as the current is interrupted its field collapses. The field that exists around all moving current is then transferred. It's an inducing force. And it induces a current in the adjacent space. As long as current is intermittent it has field propagation.

At the turn of the century, Nicolo Tesla arrived to explain the efficiency of alternating or pulsed electrical current. Pulsed electrical current transfers very well, because the field collapses along the conductor and reinduces the flow of electricity. As long as you pulse, it can traverse great distances with low ohmic resistances, and with an impedance that can be calculated and planned from the material at a frequency. Today we can transfer current great distances with AC.

The DC light bulb was invented by Thomas Edison. DC current was the first conveyer of electricity through wires. But with direct current electricity could travel no more than a mile and a half. The Westinghouse company using AC was able to send juice from Niagara Falls to cities in New York State, because of the fall in the resistance to current. The resistance in DC causes heat and resistance to its flow. But AC current overcomes that. It has its own form of resistance which is more trivial in terms of impeding the current. We call it impedance.

A reciprocal electrical network gets all its signals from its own components without an outside electrical source such as a battery. Many large biological molecules have electronic character such as capacitance or inductance. In the case of capacitors, voltage always lags the current flow. In the case of inductors, current always lags the voltage flow. These lags produce pulsed or intermittent peaks in the electrical signals. For example, I found sodium potassium ATPase has a frequency of six Herz.

When I looked at the data I realized that the DNA had .several resonant frequencies. Thus DNA becomes not only information storage but resonant energy too. DNA sets up the critical resonant frequencies of a cellular pulse. Then, over time, there is the emergence of a tissue pulse, and organ pulses, and neurologic pulses. We must look at these resonances if we are to understand what is uniquely alive. There is a reciprocal network of molecular echoes behind the physiologic pulse.

The DNA resonates with charge. It has harmonics, like a string quartet.

To get anything to move efficiently, like say a surfer on a wave, you wait for the wave that can carry the kick and paddle, so that the sine peaks overlap, and the energies carry each other. This is how the pulse works. This is how any harmonics works. The only nonchaotic, nonturbulent way of transferring energy efficiently is by overlapping crests of the peaks of these energies. This is the resonance of the organism. The intrinsic beat of the DNA is 55 beats a minute, in the case of calf thymus DNA. The beat diminishes with Digoxin, and rises with Nor-adrenaline.

The organism is a pulsed system. It is studied by a system of technology and chemistry exquisitely designed by the corrosion engineers and the corrosion electrochemists to examine the frequency response of molecules in solution.

Before working with the palladium complex in the 1990's, I simply believed that energy flowed and you could study conventional biochemical mechanisms to see how it flowed, and the whole thing could be integrated with the genetic apparatus. Somehow the flow of energy was tied to the cellular state. There was an inside called a gene and there was an outside. Everything had to eat and had to know starvation, dryness, heat, and stress. And I believed that the cell had integrated its energy pathways with its information so that it could respond when it ran out of fuel.

I had the idea initially that the energy would go one direction or another, but I thought originally that we were trying to pull charge from DNA. I thought of pulling charge from DNA long before I thought of sending charge to DNA. Of course the direction of the energy must initially be into the cell, and into the DNA. Now we know that juice should go from fats to DNA and to receptors and to collagen by way of pro-collagen. There's an enormous amount of circuitry in the body. It has to be defined. Organic metabolic conversion is the great biochemical sequence of the body. As electron transfer comes in, we add, for the first time, energy transfer through the system that is of an electronic nature, and which has very little binding. The whole convention for drug interaction has been binding (at the binding site). When we switch to electronic discharge, the coefficient of binding is 10^{-15} seconds. So it's not really binding any more. It's a bounce, it's a spark. Your spark plug is not bound to your piston. It just sparks it. Similarly, electro-active drugs are not bound to their receptors. Even though they need their receptors, they just spark them. The current is modulated, much like through a transistor. There's a burst of energy. There isn't binding in the sense of a structure. There is only binding in the recognition sense.

Originally the people who studied photosynthesis were interested in how plants captured the light and then converted it to bond energy to make sugars. This bond energy has an electrical intermediate energy state. A great deal of work was done to find out how plants do this so efficiently.

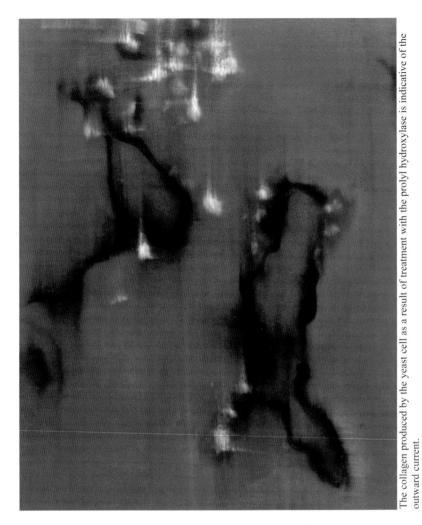

The collagen produced by the yeast cell as a result of treatment with the prolyl hydroxylase is indicative of the outward current.

A few gene sites govern a massive increase of energy within the cell and determine by this process, the special geometric changes within the earliest embryo stages.

There are a lot of electron transfer proteins such as enzymes called dehydrogenases. They carry their electrons only a very short distance within the enzyme. When you start to pass a current from one protein to another you have a much more ambitious distance to cover. It's like trying to shine a flashlight across the ocean, because the protein is not a really good conduc-

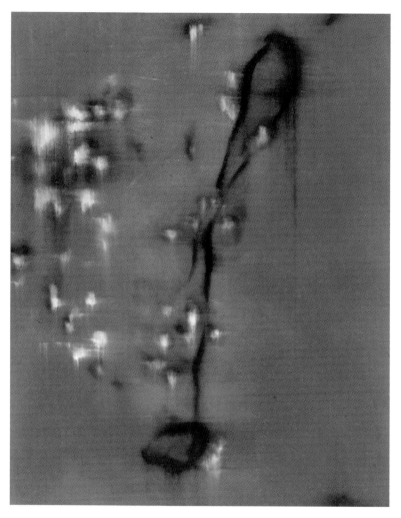

DNA over time sets up one of the critical resonant frequencies of a cellular pulse. Then, over time, there is the emergence of a tissue pulse, and organ pulses, and neurologic pulses.

tor. There's simply too much resistance. It's called the reorganization ener-gy. As the electron moves and sets up bonding with various functional groups along the protein, it has to transfer its watershell. And transferring the watershell requires a reorganization energy in the last particle that had the hydrated electron. As Marcus pointed out, this is one of the great burdens.

You have to keep restructuring your matrix, because this is not a silver wire, this is a wet protein and these are very tiny amounts of voltage. So when the donor functional group donates its electron to the acceptor, both of them have to restructure and there's a certain amount of thermal energy loss and movement loss and the whole thing doesn't go very far.

It recalls the difficulty that Thomas Edison had when trying to pump electrical current more than two miles to supply a city with his dynamos. These great generators were faced with an enormous electrical ohmic resistance. This electrical resistance could not be overcome with direct current no matter how cleverly the wires were designed. The question of raising the voltage was considered, but that created a great deal of heat.

With AC everything changes. Once you have a field, the current propagates across all surfaces. It is the water on the surface of the protein that is the conductor. The length of the molecule is less important. It is instead the electroconductive surface, with alternating current which covers distance. It's the pulse of energy produced by mitochondria rather than the flow of sugars, not the conversion of small molecules, but rather their harmonics. So once they've come on stream in the cell they all flow electrically.

Historically, theories of electron transfer have used direct current, having to do with the hydrate structure and the amount of energy necessary to displace and transfer an electron and its water molecule from donor to acceptor across a matrix which has characteristic electrical properties and characteristic differences and electron jumps and possibilities for electron tunneling. All this becomes irrelevant when you switch to AC because the parameters of electrical conduction rise to the surface of the protein and become delocalized in the field. And a field propagated along surfaces is no longer dependent on atomic centers.

Eventually I found that refined electronics can be done in liquids just as you do in a radio or television, providing your wave forms and your electronics are well modulated. We have learned to tune our molecules. We could always tune them by voltage but now were tuning them by frequency.

The intermittent nature of a current flow in a circuit arises in the capacitance and inductance of the device units. You are also aware of the existence of circuits in which an inductance and a capacitance achieve resonant frequency. We can go a little further and recall that in electronics such arrangements can allow the construction of phase locked loops. In such cases the frequency and the power transmitted can be under highly discriminating control. These solid state principles still apply in chemical and biological systems, even in the presence of water. But the measurement techniques are a little different. And the electronic devices are now biological molecules. Many of the large biological molecules can be seen as electronic capacitors. A few can be seen as inductors. I will report in the coming years, on the phase loops of the cell, and their source in the critical frequencies of the major biomolecules.

If we look at matrices that are used in insulators in capacitors, we describe their dielectric constant. The dielectric is the ability to hold charge over a distance. It's capacitance over distance. But when we do electrochemistry we don't have a homogeneous matrix or material, but rather a number of molecules dissolved in water, and we're more concerned with the capacitance of that individual molecule than the capacitance over distance. So we have a capacitance per mole. We have a mole dielectric which I call a "mole-Faraday." So we need new language to talk about the electrochemistry going on in the organism. If you have an efficient energy transfer you have to have enough energy to make an event. So you need a mole dielectric or a mole capacitance that's transferable. You have to have a donor and an acceptor and the reaction has to be measured and real, and it also has to have a biological event associated with it. You must have a bioassay that says this is worth working on, and of course, we have been doing chemotherapy and tumor treatment based on restoration of electrical charge. What makes it even more fascinating is we found that along with the charge transfer, that there is a possibility of dual kinetics; whereas one acceptor of charge will enable charge transfer, another acceptor will cause the production of radicals. And instead of a reductase-type reaction it will be a peroxidase. So there is charge transfer in one direction towards DNA. And in the other direction, using double stranded RNA or T-RNA or viral RNA, there is peroxidation. We suddenly see that nature has set up a choice for the DNA and RNA world, to go either with charge transfer or peroxidation. Peroxidation is a highly dangerous, potentially toxic modifying and selecting reaction. The proportion of DNA to RNA will make a decision in the life of this cell.

Medicines have to be more or less soluble. At the time of the discovery of the palladium complex, the question was whether you could carry on electrochemistry in water solubles at any level of efficiency. Since the palladium drug, which is water soluble, has anti-tumor activity, the answer was yes. In retrospect I believe that the charge transfer events occur in the organism just as they do in the polarograph. The charge that exists in these compounds exists on the surface hydrates of the molecules. And that hydration charge is transferable.

There is a characteristic frequency for efficient charge transfer. It occurs in the palladium compound and it occurs in DNA. There is a harmonic event and a characteristic beat for molecules that interact electrically. We can recognize music because we are music. When you tune a radio you match the wave length of the condenser to the particular wave length of the airwave. In tuning coil radios that came before solid state, you controlled the area of the condenser capacitor with a device. When you heard a station come in clearly, the interpretation was that the span frequency within the tuneable condenser compacitor was the same frequency that was coming through the airwaves. So the vibrations matched.

At a simpler level, if you join a band or an orchestra you have to keep the same beat. Basically it's a musical concept. And when you all keep time the music swells, and the roof echoes with the overlap of similar beats coming in at the same moment.

Ultimately, energy runs downhill. You're running down hill right after fertilization (right after the first pulse). When the egg starts dividing you're dying, but it's a wonderful journey and it's called development. It's all a matter of focus. In science we have an idea, and it's called equilibrium. Equilibrium means you put something in one side and part comes out the other, and in between the motor runs both ways. It's using up current. It's making heat, and if you run it too fast it may burn out. But if you didn't plug it in the first place it wouldn't develop. Many people are only interested in what they can get out of such a theory. The question is asked what can we do to live longer? But that's a private agenda. A number of researchers are working on ways to extend life, and offer theories about living forever.

I see life as having an arc, a roundedness to it. The purpose of medical research is to restore vigor and preserve health. You are, however, supposed to get out of the picture at some point, and make way for others. I believe that the organism is supposed to grow old, but it's not supposed to live sickly. It's not the responsibility of research to make people live forever, and I don't see the cellular apparatus intended to do that. Immortal organisms are all very low forms. They ferment. You can make beer, wine, and cheese with them. I think that's what immortality is for.

There is, however, a constant resurgence of life and beauty. And there is the mystery of consciousness. It is appropriate that a great mystery surrounds science. We can't and shouldn't know everything. Our task is to heal by uncovering secrets that help others to live a better and kinder life. The ultimate mysteries of life are simply not approachable through technology.

Micro photograph of the effects of the carcinogenic properties of cigarette smoke on the liquid crystal structure of palladium DNA reductase.

Discoveries come in steps. You see many things and try to bring them together while you continue to study.

7. Electrogenetics

The Liquid Crystal Faraday Effect

The first edition of First Pulse describes in some historical detail the ideas and events that led up to the discovery and patenting of Palladium DNA Reductase and the beginnings of a clinical and a research program. This has advanced steadily and in accordance with scientific traditions, peer review, and regulatory compliance. The following chapter describes the current state of my research as of September 2001. The principles of this material have recently been published in the scientific literature. The evidence for electrogenetics took time to mature and continues to unfold.

Electrogenetics refers to the energy reactions by which the living state interacts with its hereditary material. This is somewhat like a computer during uploading and downloading. The computer is turned on by its power supply, and power is continually exchanged when information is transferred back and forth from peripherals such as printers and scanners and monitors and modems. Specialized electronic frequencies and voltages are used to communicate with peripherals. The cables for these purposes have a characteristic impedance, which is to say they are usually coaxial transmission cables with selectivity for frequency propagation at specific voltages. But in the living state the transmission cables are made of long chain molecules we call polymers. The polymers that do a lot of work are prothrombin, DNA, RNA, membrane phospholipids, hyaluronic acid and procollagen. If you study these polymers individually, they are not exciting electronically. That's because they don't become efficient electronic devices until they are coated with a suitable dielectric shield. That dielectric shield is the polymer-hyaluronic acid. Once you coat prothrombin or DNA or RNA with hyaluronic acid, they carry current efficiently. This is demonstrated by performing an electronic impedance plot on the coated polymer. These plots show the now coated structures have a special phase change when current is pulsed through the solution. In this phase change the current is slowed with respect to the voltage. Such a phase change is characteristic of wires and coils as they carry a current and produce an associated magnetic field. It is called an inductance in solid state materials. In liquids it is called a *pseudoinductance*.

In electrochemical impedance spectroscopy we see the pseudoinductance plot as a complete clockwise circle. But in order to produce pseudoinductance, I was forced to invent an efficient current source to wash through the polymers. I did this by corroding a mercury drop electrode at an oxidizing voltage, and letting the mercury cations wash into the solution and electrodeposit onto the long polymer molecules. This system mimics the cation pumps of the living cell. The phenomenon of inductance in an electrical wire was first observed by Ampere, but was definitively described by

Faraday—from which we get the term *Faraday effect*. The process was described by Gauss as a transverse expulsion of current energy into the magnetic field state. It was formally presented in mathematical form by Maxwell, and later into vector notation by Heaviside. This notation is: curl B = 4 pi C. Which is to say that the net induced circulating magnetic field around an electrical wire is equal to 4 pi times the rate of current moving through the cross-section. All this sets the stage to understand what happens when the polymers interact.

Discoveries come in steps. You see many things and try to bring them together. While observing the palladium complex under the microscope, I noticed slides dry in the area at the edge of the cover slip. And, after reading Peter Collings' book on liquid crystals, I thought: we've got one of those patterns. Normally you use a cover slip when you use a microscope. If you're lucky you might notice something outside the cover slip. If you're not in too much of a hurry you might see outside the little square which holds the liquid. I had seen the fern patterns at the edge of the slide but I didn't understand what I was seeing—my thoughts were limited.

Then, I began to look at the dried portion and prepared slides without the cover slip. I watched and photographed as the material dried into the continuous liquid-crystal pattern. At first I only showed my friends and immediate associates, saying it was probably a liquid crystal. At some point, I was able to understand enough to make many slides of the palladium/lipoic complex showing continuous fern-like liquid crystal structure. Then I did experiments to identify the liquid crystallinity by subjecting the slides to magnetic fields as they dried. Under the influence of magnetic fields, the liquid crystal fern pattern is rotated and oriented into the Z axis which is the line that penetrates through the slide. These now showed a radial orientation around the field line. This response is called the *Freedericks transition*. The change identifies the substance as being field-sensitive to electrostatic or magnetic fields as are all liquid crystals.

That was a new event. After that we studied the effects of carcinogens by coating the slide with cigarette smoke before applying and drying the palladium/lipoic acid compound. The smoke produced magnificent, glowing, crystal crosses where there had been a continuous fern pattern previously. That was a breakthrough relating carcinogenesis to the destruction of liquid crystallinity.

For liquid crystallinity it's not enough to have a continuous array, you must see if the structure is altered by an electromagnetic field. What is new is that carcinogens interfere with liquid crystal formation. This suggests that substances in the body that manifest fields are easily disturbed. Tampering with liquid-crystal molecular fields risks carcinogenesis. This experiment with tobacco smoke and observations of another carcinogen, nickel 3, show that the multi-cellular state is field sensitive and field dependent. This involves the field-line density, the pulsation frequency and the voltage. The data shows that we have fields within us that provide symmetric influences over long distances. These influence not just the polymers within cells, but the cells themselves. The larger form follows its constituent forms. We have the challenge to measure the degree to which field effects alter biologic form. We realize that we have *nano-fields*, and that nano-technology is pervasive. It's a subject that's been under our nose and it is time we noticed that electronics is more than direct current and electrostatics.

The processes of an electronic schematic are based upon understanding the electronic devices in alternating current circuits, including transistors, capacitors, and inductors. The idea of electronic devices in liquids was previously improbable. When you study it, you find it yields a rich body of theory and methods.

In electrochemistry we talk about electrode reactions as being faradic. Farad is a unit of capacitance, but we say *faradic*. If you're in electronics and busy drawing schematics you put in capacitors. The electronics engineer understands capacitance as an electronic event. The electrochemist uses it as an electrode behavior related to studying corrosion. The corrosion that electrochemists are familiar with is called Warburg's corrosion where the capacitive readout of a semi-circular curve breaks down and becomes an ascending diagonal line, as the corroded ions become free in the solution.

My work now extends into an area in which electrochemistry and electronics become mixed and that is the area called pseudoinductance. Here we take our mercury electrode and allow it to corrode by setting its voltage for an oxidizing corrosion of the mercury drop. Something you should not do for a quantitative electrochemical measurement. This electro-deposition is not done in a solution of small molecules, but in a solution of long molecules such as DNA or prothrombin. In our pseudoinductance experiments, these long molecules pick up the corroded salts of the mercury and form a wire. The electrochemical impedance plot of this system plots in a reverse curve called pseudoinductance. The long molecules now act as wires to show the Faraday effect. There is generation of a magnetic field, which is paid for in current density, while recording the electronic phase (ratio of the angular velocities of current and voltage). The curve now reverses direction. The first semi-circular arc behaved as a capacitor and has voltage retardation, but the second semi-circular arc reverses phase and doubles back in direction. Because our recordings are plotted by their current/voltage velocities, there is a change in direction from capacitance to inductance, from electrostatic polarization density to magnetic field density. This has to be understood conceptually. Up to the reversal it's electrochemistry. After the reversal it's theoretical, because we corrode the electrode. And, in this case, even though the DC resistance and the frequency imposed resistance are in symmetric relation (Bode plot), the corroding electrode contributes energy from a shifting

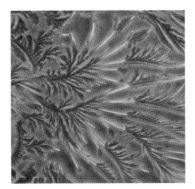

Figure 1: Prothrombin liquid crystal.

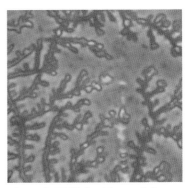

Figure 2: DNA liquid crystal showing curved and angular branches.

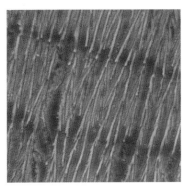

Figure 3: Prothrombin coated with hyaluronic acid.

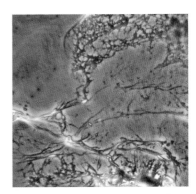

Figure 4: Effect of cigarette smoke on prothrombin-hyaluronic acid.

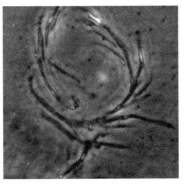

Figure 5: Effect of nickel 3 on prothrombin-hyaluronic acid.

baseline that is difficult to calculate.

Certainly chemistry, even electrochemistry and physics are separate communities of knowledge and practice. But even though research is carried on in separate communities it's important to have these communities because we have to agree on methods and literature and formalism so that we can measure together and compare and refine. So we use separate measurements, and we have separate readings, and we become experts in techniques. The problem with becoming a specialist in techniques is that you become a specialist in understanding and we should never limit our understanding. The problem with living in the Cartesian revolution is that we have cut up things in order to understand them. Sometimes we study one piece and another person studies another piece and then we need a third person to come in and study the two together and complete the historical process.

We can call one part the solid state and the second the liquid state. The challenge is to bring the electronic or solid state understanding into the heterogeneous and multi-liquid state of the body. Now as we design experiments in liquid crystals, we move into that area in which both solid state and liquid state have merged.

Recently, I demonstrated in the electrochemical literature that there is direct physical-chemical interaction between the liquid crystal states of important biological substances. Among these substances are DNA, and the blood protein prothrombin. These interactions are long range forces using the frequency dependent aspects of magnetic field energy. This is the tip of the iceberg, but it is enough to introduce the mechanism by which large molecules in the body exchange energy and signals. These large molecules or polymers (fig.1) have crystal-like structure and behavior, even as they exist dissolved in water. This state, called liquid crystal or mesophase, is comprised of uniform subunit structures comparable to any crystal. These subunit structures are also arranged in a uniform geometry comparable to a crystal, but with curved arrays (fig. 2) in addition to angular arrangements. In conventional crystals used as computer oscillators, the stimulated signal behavior is called *piezoelectric*. In liquid crystals, the energy stimulated emission of signals is called *flexoelectric*. Some biological liquid crystals form cable shaped structures when they are coated with hyaluronic acid (fig. 3).

This becomes interesting because we are searching for the signaling mechanism by which cells migrate together to form tissues and organs. The cancer cell state is a single cell type of behavior which does not form tissues and organs. The organizing communications are missing. How are these communications interrupted ?

In clear microscopic images I have shown that two carcinogens, tobacco (fig. 4) and nickel-3 (fig. 5), are each capable of destroying the liquid crystal geometry of prothrombin. The blood protein prothrombin is the circulating liquid crystal of the body. It is dynamically located as an organizing substance. Its electronic field character (Faraday inductance) can receive and transmit signals with the genetic apparatus of all cells. Its delicate field is easily deformed by toxins and carcinogens. Carcinogenic changes in DNA can now be seen as deformities in the DNA field-energized structure and signal function. I have developed synthetic catalysts which increase the density of charge in DNA, and enable the expression of the DNA liquid crystal state. Restoration of the normal field behavior of DNA and prothrombin continues to be a safe and novel approach to cancer therapeutics.

Field Effects

We often use the term electromagnetic. Now we have to look more closely at that term to see that the two halves "electro" and "magnetic" interact but are very different. An electrostatic field is a surface charge. It may be on a point but when it contacts a surface it distributes itself on that surface. It is a charge which at a point radiates with radial or spherical symmetry outward. On contact with surfaces, it will distribute itself along those surfaces. In a vacuum or in air, it will maintain its classical symmetry but if you put it in liquids or heterogeneous materials it will distribute itself over the molecules and the atoms of that material. Therefore its geometry is easily deformed or becomes identical to the surfaces of the material it transfers to. And therefore, it will not penetrate great distances as a long-range force. Thus electrostatic forces are quite limited in terms of their penetration over distance in heterogeneous material. Magnetic forces are quite different. They penetrate liquids and solids and mixtures. They will not be stopped or focused or captured until they come to a paramagnetic or ferromagnetic site. So they are the long-range forces we're looking for. If you keep in mind that magnetic and electrostatic have two different kinds of behavior in different media, then we can begin to understand the challenge of organizing cells into tissue and organs. Both kinds of forces can contribute, but in heterogeneous media the electrostatic ones are close up and the magnetic ones are long range. In addition we should gain some familiarity with the devices and circuitry that produce these.

Capacitors store electrostatic energy and allow it to oscillate in the bi-directionality of an alternating current circuit. Coils and wires with a current transferring through them form a magnetic field in the surround. This is in the great tradition of physics. Maxwell's laws derived from the work of Ampere and Gauss are numeric expressions which describe these relationships. We realize that we have to understand circuits to describe the organization of biochemical reactions. We have to look at DNA and certain proteins and their behavior according to the laws of electrostatics and the laws of magnetics.

A liquid crystal is an intermediate between a liquid and solid. It is a flexible symmetric array and dispersible in liquids. It has a liquid crystal subunit comparable to an ordinary crystal subunit. When it is deformed it produces a current. We call this the flexo-electric current. When a conventional crystal is deformed it propagates a charge and this is called piezoelectric current. Many biochemical polymers are liquid crystals. These are certain long chain molecules in the living system. They include certain proteins, DNA, RNA, and phospholipids. We know what happens when they're bent or twisted or compressed. And when energy is added to them we now understand that energy can be propagated by electronic mechanisms that operate in the physical structure and physical configurations.

Prothrombin may be a main mediator of liquid crystal phenomena in the body. It is a clot forming protein found in the blood and therefore pumped throughout the body. This is one of the unifying chemical reactions that must occur in a higher form, and that is to form the clot to repair a wound. The phenomenon of repairing a wound brings the fundamental nature of a multicellular organism to the forefront. It is organized to protect in a diffuse way, those cell systems that are part of the organism.

Earlier I looked at wound repair as a possible key to understanding what was missing in malignant cells. Wound repair is fundamental to the definition of a multi-cellular organism, and its distinction from protozoa and malignant cells. The liquid-crystal structure of prothrombin has a beautiful floral structure and an ability to respond to fields and become parallel cable structures. In those cables and their response to structures such as DNA we see communication fundamental to differentiation and maturation. When a cell is part of a wound repair system it does not work alone. It works in concert. The concert is played by polymer interactions. In addition to the known biochemical and enzymatic reactions that occur in a clot and in a scar we know that there are certainly fields present. Magnetic and electrostatic processes are going on through which cells communicate with the vascular system. There is a kind of vascular *Internet* in which cell signals are shared, and pathways and movements of cells summate and converge. This biological Internet is the focus of our present research, and the techniques and findings will be reported in the coming year.

A progress report on the analysis of tumor cell-specific killing by the Garnett McKeen Laboratory lipoic acid/palladium complex

Paul M. Bingham
Department of Biochemistry and Cell Biology
State University of New York at Stony Brook

Introduction
This document describes our progress to date in analyzing anti-tumor activity by the Garnett McKeen Laboratory lipoic acid/palladium (LAPd) complex. These studies were undertaken with the mandate from Garnett McKeen to approach LAPd killing from a molecular and cell biology perspective independent of any presuppositions about the mechanism of LAPd action. The document is organized in two sections as follows.

Section 1 - Overview of progress
This section will briefly synopsize the implications of our studies to date. It is designed to provide a brief, accessible overview. Our studies provide a strong, coherent body of evidence suggesting that transformation-specific changes in energy metabolism - most likely in the pyruvate dehydrogenase (PDH) complex - create the target that, in turn, allows the LAPd complex to specifically kill tumor cells. No other known potential cancer chemotherapeutic agent exploits this attractive target and the Garnett McKeen LAPd thus appears to be a fundamentally novel agent.

Section 2 - Detailed summary of background and progress
This section will review the background to and the most important results of our studies to date indicating that the Garnett McKeen LAPd is a potentially powerful, novel cancer chemotherapeutic agent.

Section 1 - Overview of progress
The results of our experiments to date are summarized here and described in detail in section 2 (below). The collective implication of these results is that killing of tumor cells by the Garnett McKeen Laboratory lipoic acid/palladium complex (LAPd) is highly specific and very likely to result from targeted inhibition of a tumor-specific isoform (or modification state) of the pyruvate dehydrogenase agent. These insights, in turn, indicate that LAPd may be a powerful, novel cancer chemotherapeutic agent. The essential observations are as follows.

First, our studies demonstrate that the lipoic acid/palladium (LAPd) complex component of the Garnett McKeen Laboratory mixture is the sole source of bioactivity in our cultured cell assays.

Second, the structure of LAPd suggests that one of the very small number of lipoic acid-containing cellular proteins - including the E2 and X components of the pyruvate dehydrogenase (PDH) complex - are likely targets for LAPd killing.

Third, seventy years of study have demonstrated that cancer cells have a highly altered energy metabolism in comparison to normal cells - including increased glycolysis and a shift to the use of glutamine to drive the TCA cycle.

Fourth, these earlier studies implicate alteration in the behavior of PDH as a primary source of this tumor-specific alteration of energy metabolism.

Fifth, other early studies strongly suggest that tumor-specific alteration of energy metabolism represents the activation of a wound-healing cellular program. Moreover, the functioning of this program in the intact animal likely involves a pericrine feedback-like process in which tumor cells both provoke deposition of a highly charged wound extracellular matrix (ECM) and, in turn, react to the presence of this specialized ECM.

Sixth, we have developed an efficient cultured cell system in which LAPd produces highly specific cell killing. Using this system we find that LAPd produces specific killing of transformed cells that are adherent to highly charged surfaces but not cells that are adherent to relatively uncharged surfaces. This is highly provocative in light of the properties of tumor ECM (above).

Seventh, we find that cells are substantially sensitized to LAPd killing by partial deprivation for either glucose or glutamine. Given the idiosyncratic roles of these two carbon/energy sources in tumor cells (above) this represents strongly suggestive evidence that an altered PDH is the target for LAPd killing.

Eighth, we find that capacity of mitochondrial membranes to maintain characteristic transmembrane potential is strongly and specifically reduced in sensitive cells in the presence of LAPd. PDH function is expected to be required to maintain mitochondrial membrane potential under these conditions and these data represent strong additional evidence that PDH is the target for LAPd cell killing.

Ninth, given likely tolerance for and adaptive response to partial inhibition of PDH function, the hypothesis that PDH is the target of LAPd killing predicts a nonlinear dose/response profile. This is observed. LAPd killing of sensitive cells shows an extremely sharply sigmoidal dose/response profile with a transition from no discernible effect to completely efficient killing of sensitive cells through a 2-3 fold increase in LAPd concentration.

Tenth, incorporation of LAPd onto its target protein(s) (most likely the PDH E2 and/or X proteins) through a lipoic acid residue is likely to be required for killing. Moreover, PDH is a stable protein complex - turning over slowly. We therefore further predict highly unusual kinetics for killing. This is observed as follows. At all doses above the threshold for killing, cells show no effect for ca. 18 hours, followed by a morphologically idiosyncratic arrest (below) for an additional 24 hours followed by cell death. Throughout the period before death - including the entire period of idiosyncratic arrest - cell killing is fully reversible by simply replacing the medium with LAPd-free medium. After such a medium replacement the morphologically idiosyncratic arrest slowly reverses (over ca. 24 hours) and the cells resume normal growth. This pattern of killing is extremely unusual and provides additional circumstantial support for the hypothesis that LAPd is incorporated into the PDH (or similar) complex. This is expected to produce inhibition sufficient for killing only after an extended period required for a sufficient fraction of cellular PDH to become derivatized followed by an extended period of PDH inhibition and arrest culminating in cell death.

Eleventh, PDH inhibition is expected to produce an idiosyncratic set of effects and these are observed as follows. The lag-arrest-slow death pattern seen above is expected from inhibition of energy metabolism. Moreover, PDH inhibition is expected to produce an idiosyncratic set of effects and these are observed as follows. The lag-arrest-slow death pattern seen above is expected from inhibition of energy metabolism. Moreover, PDH inhibition is expected to prevent sterol biosynthesis, thereby preventing new plasma membrane synthesis. Under these conditions cells are expected to arrest specifically at late cytokinesis. This is seen in a very large fraction of sensitive cells resulting in one of the highly idiosyncratic morphological features of LAPd arrested cells (Section 2).

Section 2 - Detailed summary of background and progress
(1) Systematic alteration of energy metabolism in cancer cells including extreme alteration of behavior of the PDH complex:

A large series of studies in the 70 years since Warburg's original discovery have shown that most cancers (carcinomas and sarcomas) show profound perturbation of energy metabolism (L.G. Baggetto, 1992, Biochemie 74, 959-974 and references therein). Together with the more recent identification of target genes for mutational alteration during origin and progression of tumors, this represents the most robust and well-documented correlate of malignant transformation. In spite of this, remarkably, the systematic alteration of tumor cell energy metabolism is essentially entirely unexploited as either a novel therapeutic target or a novel source of further insight. I will argue throughout this section that our results to date represent very strong evidence that the Garnett McKeen Laboratory's LAPd reagent is the first potential therapeutic agent to be developed that targets this altered tumor cell energy metabolism.

More specifically, the relevance of this extensive body of analysis here is that function of the PDH complex is profoundly altered in tumor cells in a way that is essential to their malignant growth and that may provide a route for selective killing or arrest of tumor cells. Our results described in succeeding sections strongly suggests that the LAPd complex may be an agent capable of such specific killing. The essential results of these earlier studies is as follows.

First, tumor cells use glucose largely glycolytically - that is, without subsequent use of glucose-derived pyruvate through the TCA cycle - even in the presence of high concentrations of molecular oxygen.

Second, this "glycolytic" bias results in large fractions of glycolytic pyruvate being disposed of in several alternative ways. One is through conventional generation of lactate; however, a second major pathway involves the joining of two pyruvate derivatives to form the neutral compound acetoin. This second pyruvate removal pathway does not require reducing potential and thereby allows glycolysis to be used to generate net yields of both reducing potential and ATP in tumor cells.

Third, this tumor-specific generation of acetoin is catalyzed by the PDH complex and requires tumor-specific PDH. PDH from untransformed cells catalyzes this reaction very poorly or not at all. Whether this tumor-specific behavior of PDH results from regulatory modification of PDH complex components - for example, by phosphorylation - or isozyme addition/replacement of one or more complex components is currently unknown.

Fourth, ATP and reducing potential are still generated through the TCA cycle in cancer cells. However, this involves a variant TCA cycle depending on glutamine as the primary energy source. Tumor-specific PDH also functions in this variant TCA cycle in tumor cells, one enzyme - the tumor-specific PDH complex - remains essential for all large-scale generation of ATP and reducing power.

Fifth, it is important to notice that this tumor-specific pattern of energy metabolism is likely organized to permit growth under the anoxic and hypoxic conditions that metastatic tumor cells frequently experience. While this functional organization could, in principle, evolve de novo in every malignancy this is quite unlikely. More plausible is the hypothesis that this altered organization reflects the illicit activation of a cellular developmental pathway designed to support the growth of normal cells under naturally occurring anoxic/hypoxic conditions. Such conditions are likely to arise when local vascularization is incomplete - especially during wound healing. The observations described in the following section strongly support this view.

(2) Tumors as wounds that will not heal: In light of the systematic alteration of tumor cell energy metabolism (above) it is extremely important to note that there is a large body of evidence that solid tumor growth (primary tumors and metastases) mimics aborted wound healing in a large number of details. This literature has been extensively reviewed previously (see G.F. Whalen, 1990, Lancet 336, 1489 and references therein) and I will briefly summarize the essential observations as follows.

First, wound healing proceeds through an ordered series of steps. These include initial generation of a fibrin clot followed by various cells including fibroblasts which lay down a temporary wound matrix. This wound matrix is characterized by high levels of heavily charged components including hyaluronic acid, chondroitin and dermatan sulphate proteoglycans. The behavior of cells in the healing wound - including mobility and secretion of matrix and matrix proteases - is strongly influenced by this charged wound matrix and these interactions thereby represent local pericrine/autocrine-like regulatory loops. As wound healing progresses the wound matrix composition gradually changes culminating in a relatively neutral normal or scar tissue matrix. This process is regulated in complex and incompletely understood ways by cytokines and related molecules which ultimately control vascularization, leakage of fibrin from local capillaries and matrix destruction/deposition. Completion of the process results in stable, continuous, vascularized tissue at the original wound site.

Second, solid tumors behave as if they are healing wounds that permanently arrest at the "wound matrix" stage of wound healing. Among other things, solid tumors recruit fibroblasts and endothelial cells. Moreover, they provoke ongoing high-level fibrin leakage from surrounding capillaries and persistent deposition of highly charged wound matrix throughout the tumor.

Third, a number of the genes known to be mutationally altered in advanced metastatic cancers are also genes implicated in the control of cellular behavior during wound healing.

In summary, the data described here and in the preceding section very strongly suggest that malignant cells constitutively express a wound healing program that this, in turn, results in altered energy metabolism and the production of an autocrine/pericrine response to highly charged wound matrix.

(3) The Garnett McKeen Laboratory Lipoic acid/palladium complex (LAPd): Our group has not been involved in the structural studies of the LAPd complex and I will not review the details of that work here. However, several details from the as yet incomplete analysis of LAPd structure by the Garnett group and collaborators are relevant as follows: First, the LAPd complex apparently contains several lipoic acid molecules and several palladium atoms (most likely three of each) joined in a coordination complex or related structure.

Second, a thiamine molecule may be associated reversibly with the complex. Because of the uncertainty of thiamine association it will not be considered further here. However, I emphasize that all of the interpretations and models described below are equally plausible independently of whether thiamine is an important element of the functional LAPd reagent. [Note that all the major lipoic acid-containing protein complexes - including PDH - also use thiamine derived coenzymes.]

Third, likely structures of the LAPd reagent suggest that it has efficient access to cytosolic and mitochondrial cellular compartments - either as a result of diffusion of the relatively hydrophobic complex through membranes and/or as a result of uptake through lipoic acid transporters.

Fourth, likely structures of the LAPd reagent are consistent with one or more of its lipoic acid residues being available for incorporation/addition to proteins - for example, PDH subunits - while remaining complexed with one or more palladium atoms. The implication of this is that LAPd may be able to deliver an inhibitory or actively toxic analog of lipoic acid to one or more cellular sites. Moreover, the LAPd may deliver a set of several such lipoic acids to a set of nearby sites - for example, in the multimeric PDH complex - as a result of its multimeric structure. [On this view, the specificity of LAPd killing might result from differential addition of LAPd lipoic acids to tumor-specific isoforms of a lipoic acid containing protein(s).]

Lastly, several experiments described below were carried out with the complex mixture of reagents - including LAPd - prepared by the Garnett group. However, the essential experiments - including glass-adherence dependence and dose/response pattern - have been repeated with the LAPd complex alone. These results indicate that all essential properties of the more complex mixture that are detectable in our cultured cells system are attributable entirely to the LAPd complex. No other components of the complex mixture have any effects detectable in this assay.

(4) The LAPd complex produces highly specific killing of immortalized cells growing on highly charged substrates: With dose/response properties to be described in the following subsection, the LAPd complex kills both highly transformed human cervical carcinoma cells (HeLa) and immortalized CV-1 cells under very specific conditions. When these cells are grown in spinner culture or on relatively neutral substrates - plastic or pyrex glass - they are apparently entirely impervious to LAPd up to the highest tested concentrations.

112

In contrast, when either of these cell lines is plated on coverslips they are killed very specifically by the LAPd complex above the critical dose. [Coverslips are manufactured from "low quality" glass which has a relatively high level of heavily charged silicates and related compounds. In contrast, pyrex glass has lower levels of such charged components.]

Because this phenomenon was initially unexpected and potentially highly informative, we have investigated it in some detail. These results indicate beyond significant ambiguity that direct attachment of cells to the charged glass substrate is the relevant variable. The following subset of our results illustrates this.

First, cells can be tested on a plastic plate containing a single small shard of glass (covering less than 1% of the plate surface area) or a large coverslip (covering ca. 90% of the plate area) and in both cases all cells attached to the glass are killed and no cells attached to the plastic are killed. Cells separated from the glass by any distance - including less than one micron - are never killed.

Second, at plating capillarity draws a significant number of cells under the coverslip. These cells attach to the plastic substrate but are covered by the extensive, continuous layer of coverslip glass separated from the cells by only a very thin layer of medium (of the order of 1-5 microns). These cells are never killed.

These studies are highly provocative in light of the nature and role of highly charged wound matrix in tumor formation and growth. We propose that adherence to highly charged coverslip glass mimics the presence of highly charged wound matrix and is essential to fully induce the cellular program that renders cells susceptible to LAPd killing.

For all studies described in the following sections cells are plated on coverslips in plastic dishes. Under these conditions both cells in untreated dishes and the plastic-adherent cells in the treated dishes represent powerful control populations. All effects described are seen only in glass-adherent cells and not in either control population.

(5) LAPd killing shows a sharply sigmoidal dose/response profile: LAPd dose/response profiles for killing show the following pattern with both HeLa and CV-1 cells. [Note that all concentrations given are calculated on the basis of inputs to the initial LAPd synthesis as provided by the Garnett group and refer to concentrations of the lipoic acid/palladium complex. These estimates are subject to significant revision by future experiments in which concentrations of active components are directly measured. The dose/response profiles and patterns of arrest and cell death for HeLa and CV-1 are identical with the exception that CV-1 cells die approximately 20% more rapidly than HeLa in some experiments. The timing of arrest and cell death described here and in the following subsection are for HeLa.]

All assays are carried out as follows. Cells are plated at low densities (typically 1/20th saturation) and allowed to adhere for 12-18 hours. LAPd is added and the plates are inspected over ca. four day interval required for control plates to grow to saturation.

The dose/response profile is as follows. First, LAPd concentrations at or below 50 micrograms/ml produce no discernible effect. Cells grow at or very near the same rate as untreated controls throughout the assay interval. These cells can be split and replated with apparently unaffected survival.

Second, at LAPd concentrations at or above 125 micrograms/ml glass-adherent cells arrest within ca. 18 hours after LAPd addition and show a highly idiosyncratic, characteristic sequence of subsequent responses culminating in cell death several days later. [See following section for detailed description.]

Third, at LAPd concentrations between 50 and 125 micrograms/ml cells show a transient response as follows. They undergo some arrest and begin to show early signs of the process leading to cell death (below) including slight rounding during the second day after LAPd addition. However, these effects usually reverse themselves and the cells recover and grow to saturation without apparent additional effect. Unlike concentrations below 50 and above 125 micrograms/ml (preceding paragraphs) responses in this concentration range show some plate-to-plate variability with some plates showing limited cell death and others showing none. This presumably reflects small experimental variation in LAPd concentration and suggests that the threshold for LAPd killing may be extremely sharp.

I will discuss the likely significance of this unusual dose/response profile after presentation of additional details in the following subsections.

(6) LAPd killing involves a complex, informative series of steps: At or above the threshold concentration for killing LAPd produces a highly informative series of responses in glass-adherent cells that culminates in their death. This sequence of steps is as follows:

First, cells arrest within ca. 18 hours of LAPd application. This arrest frequently occurs at late cytokinesis producing characteristically paired cells connected by a narrow cytoplasmic tube containing a "midbody" structure normally existing only very transiently near the end of cytokinesis (see Figures 1 and 2 below).

Second, arrested cells are slightly rounded as indicated by their appearance under phase contrast microscopy (Figures 1 and 2). Similar slight rounding is seen in normal cells during late cytokinesis and this may simply be a byproduct of arrest at this stage.

Third, these slightly rounded, arrested cells remain alive (below) and adherent for an additional 24 hours. They then round quickly to a nearly spherical shape, detach from the substrate and die. This final stage of death does not occur synchronously - cells survive with a half-life of ca. 12 hours until all ultimately die.

Fourth, all plastic-adherent cells on treated plates and all cells on nontreated plates continue to double throughout this five day period until plate surfaces are saturated.

Fifth, at any time during the treatment up to the point where a cell rounds fully and loses attachment LAPd killing is reversible. For example, if plates are treated with lethal LAPd concentrations for ca. 2 days - so that a substantial fraction of glass-adherent cells have rounded and died - followed by replacement with LAPd-free medium, most or all of the arrested but still adherent cells resume dividing after a delay of 12-24 hours in which normal morphology is recovered. These cells grow through to saturation and can be split and replated apparently as efficiently as untreated controls.

Most generally what these results indicate is that LAPd killing involves a brief lag; followed by protracted, idiosyncratic and reversible arrest; followed finally by cell death. This clearly indicates a specific class of effect - reversible inhibition of a cellular process(es) that is essential for growth, dispensable for short term survival but essential for growth and long term survival.

More specifically, these data and the unusual dose/response pattern of LAPd killing (above) indicate the following. The LAPd target(s) must be sufficiently saturated to achieve effect. At concentrations above saturation cells must be exposed to the reagent for ca. 18 hours before visible effect is observed and this effect can be reversed if the reagent is removed.

Detailed models accounting for these and other properties of LAPd killing will be discussed below.

(7) LAPd killing is associated with poisoning of energy metabolism: The following results indicate that LAPd substantially poisons energy metabolism in sensitive cells in a fashion implicating the PDH complex as a target for the reagent. The essential background and results are as follows.

First, an electrochemical potential is normally maintained across the mitochondrial membrane and is used to drive ATP synthesis. This potential is normally driven by the energy extracted during TCA cycle function - allowing the TCA cycle to drive ATP synthesis. However, ATP produced in other ways (primarily glycolysis) can be used, in turn, to drive membrane polarization. [The reasons - mechanistic or teleological - for this are unclear. However, this behavior could result from simply running the reversible ATP synthesis reaction backwards - the net free energy change associated with ATP synthesis may be small enough to permit this.]

Second, it is possible to monitor the efficiency or rate of mitochondrial membrane polarization - and, thus, the efficiency of energy metabolism - in cells as follows. A class of dyes - including rhodamine-123 - have two relevant properties here (see L.V. Johnson, et al., 1980, PNAS 77, 990-994). They bind to mitochondrial membranes and fluoresce in approximate proportion to membrane polarity. Moreover, ultraviolet irradiation of cells in the presence of these dyes causes loss of membrane potential in a process known as photodynamic depolarization. [The detailed biophysics of this effect is not understood; however, the activated dye complex may provide a route for transmembrane movement of one or more gradient components.] Thus, the rate of decay of rhodamine-123 fluorescence under conventional epifluorescent illumination provides an estimate of the rate of ATP/membrane potential generation.

Third, we find that glass-adherent cells in the presence of lethal concentrations (above) of LAPd show much more rapid (ca. 4-10 fold) rhodamine-123 photodynamic depolarization than do control cell populations. This result indicates that most or all of the major sources of mitochondrial membrane potential - likely including both glycolysis and the TCA cycle - are significantly inhibited in the presence of effective LAPd concentrations. The only known enzyme that participates in both glycolysis (pyruvate removal) and the TCA cycle in malignant cells is PDH (above).

Fourth, if PDH function is inhibited by LAPd we anticipate that small amounts of energy would continue to be generated as follows. Glycolysis would continue to generate some ATP allowed by pyruvate conversion to lactate and tumor-specific TCA cycle would continue to produce some energy by shuttling intermediates out of the mitochondrion where necessary. Thus, if LAPd is inhibiting PDH function we predict that reduction in either glucose (for glycolysis) and glutamine (for tumor-specific TCA cycle function) levels in the medium would substantially sensitize cells to LAPd killing. This is observed. Substantial reduction of either glucose or glutamine levels in the medium reduces the threshold concentration for LAPd killing (by ca. twofold) and greatly increases the rate of progress to cell death (most cells are dead within ca. 12 hours after initial arrest).

(8) Summary/conclusions: At this stage in the analysis our results are not sufficient to unambiguously define the target/mechanism of LAPd killing. However, available results represent a large, coherent body of evidence strongly suggesting the specific mechanism proposed in the following paragraph.

We propose that the combination of the genetic changes associated with malignant transformation and the signal represented by a highly charged growth substrate activates a tumor-specific PDH isoform. This isoform is specifically inhibited by LAPd. [This specificity could have any of several origins. For example, LAPd lipoates - together with their bound palladium - could be accepted only by tumor-specific PDH subunit(s). Alternatively, for example, addition of LAPd lipoate to PDH subunits could be much more inhibitory of tumor-specific than of normal PDH complex function.] This specific inhibition produces the highly idiosyncratic and specific killing by LAPd of malignant cells adherent to charged substrates.

In closing, I emphasize again that the altered energy metabolism of malignant cells is a conspicuous, attractive - but largely unexploited - target for cancer chemotherapy. Our results strongly suggest that the Garnett McKeen Laboratory has produced what may be the first effective agent for this purpose.

116

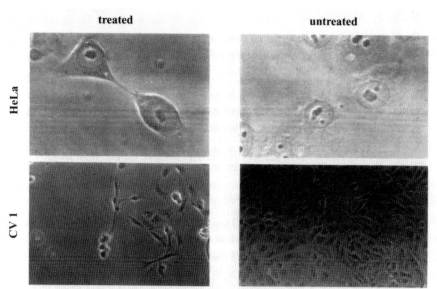

Figure 1 - LAPd killing in cultured cell system: Top: High magnification images of HeLa cells grown on cover-slips for 48 hours after addition (treated) or in the absence (untreated) of 125 micrograms/ml of the LAPd complex. Note the somewhat more refractile appearance and arrest at late cytokinesis of the treated cells. **Bottom:** Low magnification images of CV-1 cells treated as in top figure and control cells. (These cells were plated at several-fold higher density than in the experiment at the top, and the density of the untreated cells is therefore higher.) Note the much lower density (due to arrest and cell death) of the treated sample. Note also the highly refractile, fully rounded cells in the final stages leading to detachment and death. All treated, glass-adherent cells in such experiments (top and bottom) ultimately die (see text).

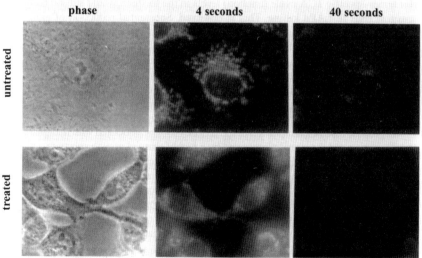

Figure 2 - Photodynamic depolarization analysis indicating that LAPd poisons energy metabolism: HeLa cells (phase contrast image at left) were photographed under epifluorescent illumination in the presence of rhodamine-123 after 4 seconds or 40 seconds of prior ultraviolet illumination. Cells were cultured for 24 hours in the presence (treated) or absence (untreated) of 125 micrograms/ml of LAPd before addition of rhodamine-123 and photography. Note that the treated sample is already less fluorescent after 4 seconds of illumination and has been bleached to essentially background levels of fluorescence after 40 seconds. In contrast, the untreated sample shows substantial mitochondrial fluorescence even after 40 seconds of illumination. From a number of experiments of this sort we conclude that LAPd treated mitochondria in sensitive cells show severalfold higher rates of photodynamic depolarization in comparison to untreated controls.